World Regional

Geography

The Essentials

Kendall Hunt
p u b l i s h i n g   c o m p a n y

Rebecca
WEST

Macomb Community College

for the Edward

He kept me from asking, "Are we there yet?" by putting a map in my small hands and teaching me how to read it. He gave me a thirst for adventure by looking for the road not yet taken and encouraging me to explore new scenic routes to my destinations every day.

My compass, my champion, my father—Edward Logan unintentionally made me a geographer, and for that I am forever grateful.

Acknowledgments

Sincere thanks to Amy Parsons and Cathie Fitz, two incredible geographers for their additions to this publication.

Earnest gratitude to Kim Davis for helping me interpret my heart's words, and to Grace Smith for collecting geographic terminology.

Contents

Chapter 3   Middle America 27

Chapter 4   South America 41

Chapter 5 Europe **55**

Chapter 6 Russia, Transcaucasia, and Central Asia **71**

FOUNDATIONS OF GEOGRAPHY

Geography is not important; it is essential… . The issues facing us today can only be understood from a geographical perspective.

—NCGE

The Study of Geography

According to the National Geographic Society, **geography** is the study of places and the relationships between people and their environments. It is a spatial discipline that explains the location (where), patterns (what and how), and interactions (why and when) of relationships on Earth.

Location

Location is the most fundamental or basic concept in geography. Location answers the question "where?" Absolute location refers to the specific, precise physical location of a place. Relative location refers to the position of a place relative to other known places.

Thomas J. Karwowski

Geography is the father of all sciences. Geography is the gateway into the different avenues of physical and social sciences. For instance, students intrigued by cultural geography may also find themselves interested in anthropology or sociology; likewise, students intrigued by biogeography may also find an interest in biology. Nearly every subset of geography has a broader science topic to explore. Due to the foothold that geography has in both scientific spheres, it is often common for students to comment on how geography ties into so much of their academic study.

Topical and Regional Geography

Geography can be studied based on topics or on regions. This text divides the world by regions to look at territories, peoples, and culture, but it also looks at a variety of topics including development, resources, and the four physical spheres—atmosphere (air), hydrosphere (water), lithosphere (land), and biosphere (life). This chapter gives a broad overview of the essentials in topical geography that will be applicable in the regional space.

Maps and Location

When most people think about geography, the first thing that comes to mind is maps. Geographers look at maps to help them understand various problems and find solutions. When reading a map and trying to find a particular point, geographers use both *absolute location* (Latitude and longitude), and *relative location* (proximity to locale).

Bangladeshi people carry drinking water after collecting it from a fresh-water source at coastal area in Khulna, Bangladesh.

Latitude and Longitude

Latitude and longitude identify absolute location on Earth through the use of imaginary lines. **Latitude** lines run east and west on the earth and are known as parallels. Lines of latitude run from 0° to 90° in the Northern and Southern Hemispheres. Therefore, it is crucial that when noting the degreed number of latitude that an N or an S be assigned. The **equator** is the key line of latitude and is the only latitudinal line that needs neither an N or an S assigned, to it as it sits at 0° latitude. The following parallels are other key lines of latitude typically identified.

- The Tropic of Cancer (23.5° N) and the Tropic of Capricorn (23.5° S).
- The Arctic Circle (66.56° N) and the Antarctic Circle (66.56° S).
- The North Pole (90° N) and the South Pole (90° S).

Longitude lines run north and south on the earth and are known as meridians. Lines of longitude run from 0° to 180° in the Eastern and Western Hemispheres. When noting the degreed number of longitude, it is crucial that an E or a W be assigned. The Prime Meridian, which sits at 0°, and the 180° line of longitude are the two key lines of longitude that need neither an E or a W assigned to them. Longitudinal lines are not even nor parallel like

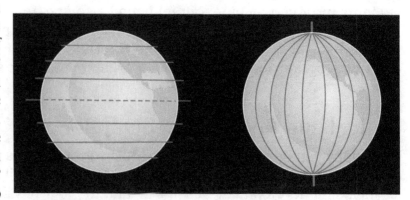

Geographic coordinate system of the globe. Latitude is a coordinate line that specifies the north-south location. Longitude is a coordinate line that specifies the east-west location.

latitudinal lines. These meridians are furthest away from each other at the equator and merge together at the north and the south poles.

Lines of longitude also help keep time, as many countries or political states identify every 15° of longitude around the world to be a new time zone, which also corresponds with 15° the earth rotates in one hour (24 time zones × 15° = 180°). The **Prime Meridian** is a key line of longitude that runs through Greenwich, England, and is where time starts. Zones west of Greenwich lose an hour on the clock and zones east of Greenwich gain an hour on the clock. The **International Date Line** (IDL),

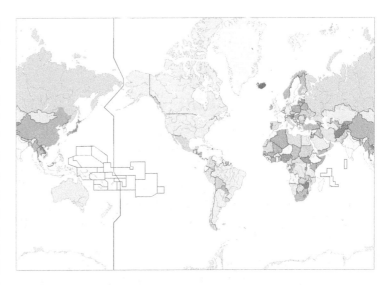

The International Date Line (IDL) twists on, or near 180° in an effort to keep countries and political states on the same day. Consider how the far eastern portion of Russia would be on a different day if the IDL didn't twist around it.

which is on or near the 180° line of longitude, is where each new day begins. Traveling eastward across the IDL causes travelers to lose a day, while traveling westward across the IDL causes travelers to gain a day.

Map Projections

It is impossible to take the data from a round earth and accurately show it on a flat map without distorting the images, but cartographers over the centuries have attempted to create their own unique map projections to preserve key features. The four key features preserved on map projections are *area, shape, direction*, and *distance*. Typically, a map projection can preserve only one or two of these features at a time. Digital maps, such as Google Earth, are getting better at lessening the distortion of these projections. However, comparing the Mercator map projection to the Mollweide map projection shows many discrepancies.

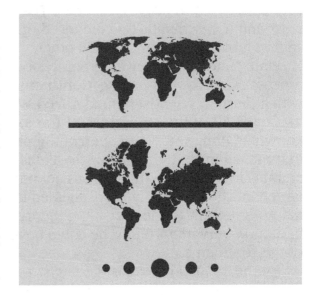

Mercator and Mollweide projection worldmaps.

Map Scale

Map scale refers to the ratio or proportion between map distance and size and real earth distance and size. Maps can be classified as either small-scale or large-scale. **Small-scale maps** show large areas with less detail. All globes and world maps are small-scale images. **Large-scale maps** show small areas with lots of detail. Topographic maps and neighborhood maps are good examples of large-scale images.

Modern Geographic Technology

In the twentieth century, with the increase of technology, geography was able to make large strides. Today, geographers use **remote sensing** (scans of Earth with aerial photography, and satellite imagery/data), **global positioning system** (GPS), and **geographic information system** (GIS) to gain the big-picture perspective on today's major geographic issues. Comparing the ice melt of glacier systems in the last few decades or the impact of a volcanic debris field on a landscape is an easier feat with modern geographic technology.

Planet earth with satellite rendered in detailed view from outer space.

Theory of Plate Tectonics

Until the 1950s, the prevailing earth science theory was of a fixed and rigid earth. Today most earth scientists believe in the **theory of plate tectonics,** one of the most important 20th century earth science theories. The theory states that the earth's **lithosphere** (the crust and upper mantle) is comprised of nine major and ten minor tectonic plates that shift or move over or under each other.

Plate tectonics theory incorporates two main components: continental drift and the process of sea floor spreading. **Continental drift** refers to a set of ideas highly associated with a German scientist named **Alfred Wegener**. In the early 1900s, Wegener proposed that once all of the land areas of the earth were joined together in a supercontinent known as **Pangaea**. This supercontinent eventually began to split apart into segments that moved or drifted. The puzzle-like fit of the continental edges, identical plants and animals in widely separated areas, identical rock types in widely separated areas, and a variety of climatic evidence all seemed to support Wegener's ideas. However, his ideas did not conform to the prevailing theory of the time that the earth was rigid and fixed in nature. Very importantly, he could never identify a force that could cause the drifting of the continents.

By the 1950s and 1960s, geologist Harry Hess was aware of the great topographic diversity of the oceans: mid-ocean mountain ridges and deep oceanic trenches along the edge of the Pacific Ocean. Based on his research, he proposed a "convection" model. He theorized that hot fluid magma was continuously being pushed upward in the earth's interior by internal forces. As this magma rose, it began to cool and harden. As it reached the mid-ocean ridges, it solidified into new sea floor, causing the pre-existing sea floor to be pushed aside. As the sea floor began to move away from the mid-ocean ridges, it caused the plates to shift or move. This process is now referred to as **sea floor spreading**. Supporting evidence based on ocean floor age and magnetism seems to strongly indicate the existence of this process. Most earth scientists now believe that sea floor spreading is the force that Wegener could not identify.

The theory of plate tectonics is closely associated with other geologic activity such as mountain-building, earthquakes, and volcanoes. Most of the earth's major mountain systems, such as the Andes, Alps, and Himalayans are connected to plate activity. A circular-shaped area around the rim of the Pacific Ocean basin is where the world's greatest concentration of volcanic and earth-

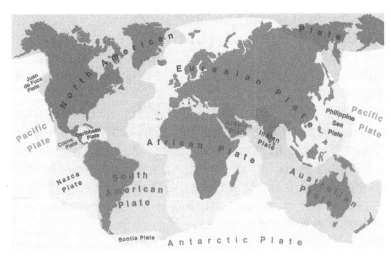

Tectonic plates of planet earth; showing the major and minor plates.

quake activity occurs. This area is known as the **Pacific Ring of Fire**, which results from dense oceanic plates' sliding beneath lighter continental plates, creating geologic instability, such as earthquakes and volcanoes.[2]

Climate Factors

Climate is the result of the interaction of a number of factors, known as climate controls. The most basic control on climate is latitude. The angle of sun's energy and the length of daylight hours are both mainly affected by latitude. Latitude essentially determines basic temperature conditions. As latitude increases, temperature tends to decrease.

Another climate control is location relative to water. Places near large bodies of water have moderate seasonal temperature changes. These are called **maritime locations** and include places like San Francisco, Seattle, and Rome. **Continental locations**, places far from large bodies of water, have great seasonal temperature changes. Continental locations include places like central Canada, eastern Europe, and most of Russia.[3]

Land heats and cools faster than water does. Climatically, this means that the large continents of the world are warmer than the oceans in their summer months and colder than the oceans in their winter months. This phenomenor further contributes to the intense winter cold experienced by the interior of the continents. Conversely, summer temperatures are as much as 50°F hotter in the interior of the continents than in coastal areas. Along the edges of most continents, the moderating influence of the oceans keeps summer temperatures down and winter temperatures relatively high.[4]

A third climate control is altitude. Air at lower altitudes is warmer and holds more moisture. Air at higher altitudes is cooler and holds less moisture. In the tropical latitudes, places at low altitudes are very warm and very wet. In the tropical latitudes, places at higher altitudes are cooler and drier.

A fourth climate control is landforms. If air encounters a landform, such as a mountain, it is forced to rise and the air cools, causing precipitation on the **windward side** of the mountain. As the air descends the other side, the **leeward side**, the air warms and dries out, creating a dry condition known as the **rain shadow effect**. In the western United States, places such as Portland and Seattle are lush and green because they are on the windward sides of the Pacific mountains. In contrast, eastern Washington and eastern Oregon are dry and brown because they are on the leeward sides of the mountains.

A last climate control is the effect of prevailing wind and ocean currents. Warm air and warm ocean currents bring in warm and wet conditions to an area. In contrast, cold air and cold ocean currents bring cold and dry conditions to an area. The southeast United States is hot and wet in the summer because of the warm Gulf Stream ocean current and winds coming from the Gulf of Mexico. The southwest coast of the United States is dry in the summer with lower summer temperatures because of the cold California ocean current and winds coming off the ocean.[5]

Climate Regions[6]

The difference between weather and climate is that **weather** is what is happening right now, while **climate** is what is supposed to be happening right now based on years of averaged data. Climatologists study the climate of the world and break it into a few main climate regions. Wladimir Köppen gave each climate region a letter designation (A, B, C, D, E, and H). A to E climate regions are nearly like belts around

World map in colors by temperature.

the world, corresponding to the climate factors and controls already mentioned. H climate zones recognize the highland or mountainous areas of the world and vary in their locations.

The **humid equatorial (tropical) climate** or "A" region, occurs in the tropics from about the equator to 25 degrees of latitude also known as ITCZ (Inter Topical Convergence Zone.) This is an area around the equator with daily convergent weather. Examples include the Amazon Basin in South America, the Congo Basin in central Africa, and the islands of Indonesia. The **dry climates,** or "B" region, occur in both tropical and middle latitude areas of the world. They are found in places such as the Sahara in northern Africa, central Australia, southwest North America, southwest South America, and central Asia. They are characterized by little annual precipitation (generally less than 20 inches per year), and there is more evaporation than precipitation. The **Humid temperate (mild) climates,** or "C" region, are found between 25 degrees of latitude and 50 degrees of latitude. Examples include most of the eastern U.S., southern and western Europe, southeast Australia, and east China. They are climates with moderate levels of temperature and precipitation that create the conditions for most agricultural production. The **humid** cold climates, or "D" region, are found in the interiors of landmasses and upper high latitude areas. Examples include Russia, Canada, far northern Europe, most of eastern Europe, and north China. The **polar climates**, or "E" region, are areas concentrated near the poles with very low temperatures and include the tundra and icecaps.

World Population

There are approximately 7.5 billion people in the world. A striking feature of this world population is its uneven distribution. Most people are found in middle latitude coastal areas in the Northern Hemisphere. There are three main world population clusters. South Asia is the most densely populated cluster, with about 25 percent of the world's population. It includes the second most populated country, India. East Asia is the second largest cluster, with almost 25 percent of the world's population. It includes China, currently the most populated country in the world. The third main cluster is Europe, including the European part of Russia. This cluster has about 15 percent of the world's population.

Population change can result from either natural change or migration. **Natural change** is the difference between fertility and mortality in a place. The most common way to measure fertility is through the **crude birth rate** (the # of births/1,000 people). The most common way of measuring mortality is through the **crude death rate** (the # of deaths/1,000 people). The difference between these two rates is the **rate of natural change** (the crude birth rate – the crude death rate, typically expressed as a percentage). The best way to measure fertility is the total fertility rate. **Total fertility rate** (TFR) refers to the average number of children a woman has between the ages of 15–44. A total fertility rate of "2.1" is known as the **replacement rate**. Over time, this rate would likely lead to population stability. Another very important way of measuring mortality is the infant mortality rate. **Infant mortality rate** refers to the number of infants/1,000 births who die before age 1.[8]

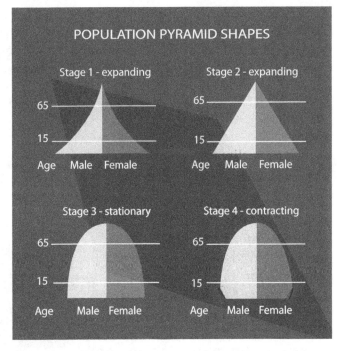

Examples of the first four stages of the Demographic Transition Model.

Demographic Transition Model

In the mid-twentieth century, a population change model was introduced—the **demographic transition model**. It is based on the actual demographic experience of European and European-related countries that have a long and accurate set of census data. The demographic transition model links population change to economic change over time in stages.

Stage 1 includes countries that are dominantly agricultural, rural, and isolated. Given these conditions, stage 1 countries have high birth rates and equally high death rates. The result is population stability but at a high level. Today, only a few isolated and very poor countries are in stage 1.

Stage 2 is the first major transition that occurs. Countries are still dominantly agricultural and rural, so birth rates remain high. However, countries are no longer isolated, and medical technology is introduced, allowing a quick and sharp decline in death rates. With high birth rates and fast falling death rates, the population grows very fast. Stage 2 is a stage of **population explosion**. Most of the less developed countries, like countries in Africa, Latin America, and much of Asia, are in stage 2.

Stage 3 is the second major transition that occurs. Death rates continue to fall, and birth rates begin to decline. The birth rate decline results from a country's undergoing a transition to industrialization and urbanization. As European and European-like countries shifted from agriculture to industry and from rural to urban life, birth rates fell. The population still grows but at a slower rate. Countries like Brazil and China are in stage 3.

Stage 4 includes countries that now are highly economically developed and dominantly urban and suburban. Birth rates are low and death rates are low, creating population stability but at a low level. Most of the more developed countries are in stage 4.

Stage 5* includes a number of more developed countries whose birth rates are so low, combined with large aging populations, that the birth rate is now below the death rate, leading to population decline. Stage 5 is a stage of **population implosion**. Some countries in Europe, along with Japan, are in an implosion stage.[9]

*Some demographers recognize only stages 1-4, and state that stage 5 is theoretical. Others recognize stage 5 as a whole new model.

World Languages and World Religions

Language is most commonly classified on the basis of its genesis or origin. **Language** includes words and pronunciation combined for human understanding for the purpose of communicating with other people. The broadest level of language classification is a language family. A **language family** is a relatively large and broad assortment of all languages related by common ancestry. The most spoken and most widespread language family is the Indo-European language family. It dominates in Europe, the Americas, most of Russia, Iran, Afghanistan, and most of south Asia.

Scholars commonly identify five main **world religions** that are widespread across the earth, with a large

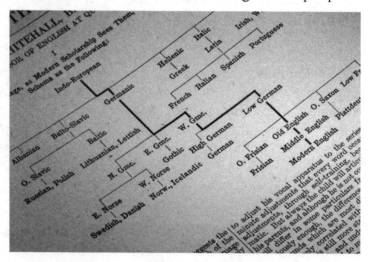

Evolution of English Language from Indo-European to Modern English

B.R.I.C - india - china
brazil russia
2nd -ing-

number of adherents. They are Christianity, Islam, Hinduism, Buddhism, and Judaism. **Christianity** is the largest and most widespread religion. It dominates in Europe, the Americas, most of the populated parts of Russia, as well as Africa below the Sahara. **Islam** is the world's second largest and second most widespread religion. It dominates in northern Africa, southwest Asia, central Asia, parts of south Asia, and Indonesia. **Hinduism** is the world's third largest religion in numbers and dominates in India and Nepal. **Buddhism** is the world's fourth largest religion in numbers and dominates in East Asia and mainland Southeast Asia. **Judaism** is relatively insignificant in numbers and dominates only in Israel.

Religion is classified in several different ways. Location, origin and dominance differentiate religion into eastern and western religions. **Eastern religions** have their origin and dominance in southern and eastern Asia. Hinduism and Buddhism are the two main world eastern religions. **Western religions** have their origin in southwest Asia. Judaism, Christianity, and Islam are the three main world western religions. On the basis of philosophy, religion is differentiated into monotheistic and polytheistic religions. **Monotheistic religions** believe in one god. Judaism, Christianity, and Islam are the three main world monotheistic religions. **Polytheistic religions** believe in many gods or spirits. Hinduism is the only main world polytheistic religion. Buddhism is not clearly classified on the basis of philosophical belief. A third type of religion classification is based on whether the religion is localized to a certain group or area without missionary activity or whether a religion is universally applicable with much missionary activity. **Ethnic religions** are localized without intense conversion activity. Hinduism and Judaism are two main world ethnic religions. **Universalizing religions** are universally applicable to anyone anywhere and are very conversion-oriented. Christianity, Islam, and Buddhism are the three main world universalizing religions.[10]

Forms of Territoriality

Territoriality is the process by which an individual or group identifies with an area, claims it as its own, and defends it if needed. Over time, several forms of territoriality have emerged. **State** is an inherently political concept, comprised of an area, recognized boundaries,

Language Extinction

About every two weeks another language dies, taking millennia of human knowledge and history with it.

A.R Williams

Major world religion symbols.

and a government in effective control of the area. Essentially, a state is a country. **Nation** is a social-cultural concept, comprised of a group of people bonded or unified by one or more items. Beginning with the French Revolution in Europe, a new form of territoriality emerged known as a nation-state. A **nation-state** is a country comprised of a unified group of people. A **unified nation-state** refers to a country where almost everyone is ethnically and culturally the same. Japan, Denmark, and Slovenia are examples of unified nation-states. The United States is broadly a unified nation-state since most Americans are unified by the English language,

200 national waving flags from all over the world.

Christian religion, and similar values, such as democracy, liberty, and freedom. A **binational state** is a country comprised of two distinct nations. Canada, Belgium, and Croatia are examples. A **multinational state** is a country comprised of three or more distinct nations. Bosnia, Serbia, and every country in Africa are examples. A **stateless nation** occurs where a nation does not have its own state. Examples include the Palestinians, the Kurds, and the Basques. Since the end of World War II, a new form of territoriality exists: a **supranational organization,** where a collection of three or more countries (states) join together for some mutual economic, military, or political purpose. The United Nations, NATO (North Atlantic Treaty Organization), the European Union, and ~~NAFTA~~ (North American Free Trade Agreement) are good examples.[11] USMC

Globalization

Globalization is a process that involves the global connections of people and places. Key characteristics include transnational corporations and global interaction and diffusion. It is a process that emphasizes free trade and involves much

The world's coolest McDonalds in Taupo, New Zealand.

cultural standardization, such as the rapid spread of McDonald's and Coca-Cola across the world. It is a very controversial process that many people claim makes the rich richer and the poor poorer, as well as creating more standardization or homogenization of cultures.

The influence of globalization is seen in clothing, shoes, cars, cell phones, and all kinds of merchandise. The world today is highly interconnected. What happens in one place has repercussions on much of the rest of the world.[12]

Economic Sectors and Development

Typically, the economy is comprised of three different sectors that are differentiated by their activities. *Primary activities* involve the extraction of raw materials directly from the environment. Agriculture, mining, fishing, and logging are primary activities.

Secondary activities include the processing of raw materials into finished products. Manufacturing, steel production, automobile production, processing of crude oil, and milling of grain into cereal products are all examples of secondary activity. *Tertiary activities* include the marketing of products, such as retailing and wholesaling. Service activities, like medicine, law, and education, are also tertiary activities.

Economic development is a process by which countries experience economic change over time. A wide range of development exists in the world today. To better understand this range of development, researchers often divide it into two main groups—the more developed countries and the less developed countries. *orange*

More developed countries (MDC) include the United States, Canada, Australia, New Zealand, Japan, South Korea, Taiwan, Singapore, Russia, and the countries of Europe. **Less developed countries (LDC)** include the countries of Middle and South America, the countries of Africa, and most of the countries of Asia.

The position of a country along the spectrum of development is identified by the use of various indicators. **Social indicators of development** include literacy and level of education. More developed countries tend to have higher rates of literacy and higher levels of formal education. Less developed countries have an opposite set of social factors. **Demographic indicators of development** include birth rate, rate of change, life expectancy, age structure, infant mortality, and total fertility rate. The one ineffective demographic factor is the death rate. More developed countries tend to have low birth rates, low or negative population change, long life expectancy, low infant mortality, and low total fertility resulting in few youth and many elderly people. Less developed countries tend to have the opposite set of factors. **Economic indicators of development** include per capita income, proportion of a population that lives in urban areas, and dominant economic sector. More developed countries tend to have high income levels, a high proportion of urban population, and dominance of services and industry. Less developed countries tend to have the opposite set of factors.[13]

What Is a Region?

A **region** is a bounded-off area that consists of similar kinds of things, such as similar climate or topography or language. It is not a phenomenon that naturally exists, but it is an intellectual or mental construct. A person recognizes a region based on his (her) subjective view of a place. It is a very important tool in geography for classifying and organizing information about the earth. Regions have locational characteristics and are territories with boundaries that can be sharply defined. Usually, boundaries are transition zones.

There are two general types of regions: *formal* (uniform) and *functional* (nodal). **A formal (uniform) region** refers to a bounded-off area of distinctive properties that are evenly or uniformly arranged. **A functional (nodal) region** refers to a bounded-off area with distinctive properties that are concentrated in a focus or node with functional connections to the periphery of the area.[14]

The seven world continents.

The World in Regions

The study of geography once centered upon the *seven continents* (North America, South America, Europe, Asia, Africa, Australia, and Antarctica) and *five oceans* (Atlantic, Pacific, Indian, Arctic, and Southern). Today, geographers like to split the world into twelve regions, although this approach ignores Antarctica and the oceans. The regions are divided based on their physical and cultural landscape similarities as follows:

- North America
- Middle America
- South America
- Europe
- Russia, Transcaucasia, and Central Asia
- East Asia
- South Asia
- Southeast Asia
- North Africa/Southwest Asia
- Sub-Saharan Africa
- Australia and New Zealand
- Oceania (Pacific Islands)

Review Terms

Alfred Wegener ✓
binational state ✓
Buddhism ✓
Christianity ✓
climate ✓
continental drift ✓
continental locations ✓
crude birth rate ✓
crude death rate ✓
demographic indicators of development ✓
demographic transition model ✓
dry climates ✓
eastern religions
economic development ✓
economic indicators of development
equator ✓
ethnic religions ✓
formal (uniform) region
functional (nodal) region ✓
geographic information system (GIS) ✓
geography ✓
global positioning system (GPS) ✓
globalization
Hinduism ✓

humid cold climates ✓
humid equatorial (tropical) climate ✓
humid temperate (mild) climates ✓
infant mortality rate ✓
International Date Line (IDL)
Islam ✓
Judaism ✓
language ✓
language family
large-scale maps ✓
latitude
leeward side
less-developed countries (LDC) ✓
lithosphere
longitude ✓
maritime locations
monotheistic religions
more developed countries (MDC) ✓
multinational state ✓
nation ✓
nation-state ✓
natural change ✓
Pacific Ring of Fire
Pangaea ✓

polar climates ✓
polytheistic religions
population change ✓
population explosion ✓
population implosion ✓
Prime Meridian ✓
rain shadow effect
rate of natural change ✓
region ✓
remote sensing
replacement rate
sea floor spreading ✓
small-scale maps ✓
social indicators of development ✓
state ✓
stateless nation ✓
supranational organization
territoriality
theory of plate tectonics
total fertility rate (TFR) ✓
unified nation-state ✓
universalizing religions
weather ✓
western religions ✓
windward side
world religions ✓

quaternary

quinary

Research Topics

biodiversity hot spot
colonialism
cultural imperialism
gross domestic product
gross national income
Kyoto Protocol
lingua franca
nonrenewable energy
population density
purchasing power parity (PPP)

Region

Place → common features:

mts   Plains
cultural   Climate

renewable energy
spatial diffusion
sustainability

Credits

1. **Source:** From Thomas J. Karwoski, *World Regional Geography: An Introduction*, 1st ed., Copyright © 2016 by Kendall Hunt Publishing Company. Reprinted by permission.
2. **Source:** From Thomas J. Karwoski, *World Regional Geography: An Introduction*, 1st ed., Copyright © 2016 by Kendall Hunt Publishing Company. Reprinted by permission.
3. **Source:** From Thomas J. Karwoski, *World Regional Geography: An Introduction*, 1st ed., Copyright © 2016 by Kendall Hunt Publishing Company. Reprinted by permission.
4. **Source:** From Alan A. Lew, C. Michael Hall, and Dallen J. Timothy, *World Regional Geography: Human Mobilities, Tourism, Destinations, Sustainable Environments*, 2nd ed., Copyright © 2015 by Kendall Hunt Publishing Company. Reprinted by permission.
5. **Source:** From Thomas J. Karwoski, *World Regional Geography: An Introduction*, 1st ed., Copyright © 2016 by Kendall Hunt Publishing Company. Reprinted by permission.
6. **Source:** From Thomas J. Karwoski, *World Regional Geography: An Introduction*, 1st ed., Copyright © 2016 by Kendall Hunt Publishing Company. Reprinted by permission.
7. **Source:** From Thomas J. Karwoski, *World Regional Geography: An Introduction*, 1st ed., Copyright © 2016 by Kendall Hunt Publishing Company. Reprinted by permission.
8. **Source:** From Thomas J. Karwoski, *World Regional Geography: An Introduction*, 1st ed., Copyright © 2016 by Kendall Hunt Publishing Company. Reprinted by permission.
9. **Source:** From Thomas J. Karwoski, *World Regional Geography: An Introduction*, 1st ed., Copyright © 2016 by Kendall Hunt Publishing Company. Reprinted by permission.
10. **Source:** From Thomas J. Karwoski, *World Regional Geography: An Introduction*, 1st ed., Copyright © 2016 by Kendall Hunt Publishing Company. Reprinted by permission.
11. **Source:** From Thomas J. Karwoski, *World Regional Geography: An Introduction*, 1st ed., Copyright © 2016 by Kendall Hunt Publishing Company. Reprinted by permission.
12. **Source:** From Thomas J. Karwoski, *World Regional Geography: An Introduction*, 1st ed., Copyright © 2016 by Kendall Hunt Publishing Company. Reprinted by permission.
13. **Source:** From Thomas J. Karwoski, *World Regional Geography: An Introduction*, 1st ed., Copyright © 2016 by Kendall Hunt Publishing Company. Reprinted by permission.
14. **Source:** From Thomas J. Karwoski, *World Regional Geography: An Introduction*, 1st ed., Copyright © 2016 by Kendall Hunt Publishing Company. Reprinted by permission.

Chapter 2

NORTH AMERICA

How do you find America? Turn left at Greenland.

—Ringo Starr

Where Is North America?

North America consists of the countries on the North American continent. North America resides in the Northern and Western Hemispheres and sits mainly on the North American tectonic plate. However, the Pacific tectonic plate and minor Juan de Fuca tectonic plate do influence activity on the western edge of this region.

North American continent with the North American region in blue.

Comparison and Contrast

This chapter primarily focuses upon the United States and Canada. The two countries are comparable in territorial size. Canada is slightly larger than the United States. Canada is the world's second largest country in land area, and the United States ranks fourth in land area.

Both countries are mainly located in the middle latitudes. Since most of Canada is north of the United States, it does include a larger area of colder, drier climate conditions.

Politically, the United States and Canada are federal states. A **federal state** is a country where power is distributed through different levels: national, state (province), county, and municipality. Both countries have a democracy-style government; Canada has a parliamentary democracy, while the United States has a representative democracy.

The two countries are very economically developed, with high income levels and high production of manufacturing. They are both very highly urbanized and maintain high levels of trade with each other.

The Aurora

The **Aurora** is a natural lightshow that occurs above the two magnetic poles when Sun's electrically charged particles enter Earth's gaseous atmosphere.

The Aurora is referred to as the *Aurora Borealis* (northern lights) in the Northern Hemisphere and the *Aurora Australis* (southern lights) in the Southern Hemisphere.

Multicolored northern lights (Aurora borealis)

Culturally, the United States and Canada are dominantly Indo-European countries that are primarily Christian in religion. English is the major language spoken in the United States, though it is not an official language of the country. In Canada, there are two official languages: English and French. Most U.S. Americans are Protestant Christian. In Canada, Catholic Christians represent a higher share of the population than in the United States. Canada does have a stronger presence of European culture and lifestyle than the United States.

The biggest contrast between the two countries is population size. There are about 328 million people in the United States; Canada only has about 37 million people.

Landform Patterns

Topographically, river, interior, and coastal plains dominate the eastern two-thirds of the United States and the eastern four-fifths of Canada. Mountains and high plateaus dominate the western parts of both countries with parallel north to south mountains.[2] The physical regions (and the subregions) of North America are as follows:

- Eastern Coastal Plains (Atlantic Coast and Gulf of Mexico Coast)
- Appalachian Mountains (Piedmont Plateau, New England, Blue Ridge, Ridge and Valley, Appalachian Plateaus, and Adirondacks)

- Canadian Shield (Shield and Superior Uplands)
- Interior Lowlands (St. Lawrence Lowlands, Interior Low Plateaus, and Central Lowlands)
- Ozark Plateau and Ouachita Mountains
- Great Plains and Prairies
- Rocky Mountains and Wyoming Basin
- Intermountain Plateaus (Colorado Plateaus, Columbia Plateaus, and Basin and Range)
- Western Mountain Ranges (Sierra Nevada, Cascade Mountains, and Cordillera)
- Pacific Border and Lower California
- Alaska
- Arctic Coastal Plains and Hudson Bay Lowlands
- The Hawaiian Islands

Climate Patterns

Most of the United States and Canada is known for having a humid climate. A humid temperate (mild) subtropical climate dominates in the southeastern U.S. There are long, hot summers and short, mild winters, with abundant precipitation through the year. New Orleans, Atlanta, and Charlotte are typical examples.

A humid temperate (mild) Mediterranean climate dominates in coastal central and southern California. Summers are warm and dry, with mild and wet winters. San Diego, Los Angeles, and San Francisco are examples.

LAKE MICHIGAN	
Maximum length	307 mi (494 km)
Maximum width	118 mi (190 km)
Surface area	22,404 sq mi (58,030 km²)
Average depth	279 ft (85 m)
Maximum depth	923 ft (281 m)
Water volume	1,180 cu mi (4,900 km³)
Surface elevation	577 ft (176 m)

Lake Michigan is the only Great Lake entirely in the USA.

A humid temperate (mild) marine climate dominates in the Pacific Northwest. Summers are cool and wet, with winters being mild and wet. Conditions include clouds, fog, and misty rain for much of the year. Seattle and Portland, Oregon, are examples.

A humid cold (continental) climate dominates in New England and the Great Lakes areas. Summers tend to be shorter and cooler with long, cold winters. Boston and Chicago are examples. This climate primarily dominates across the majority in Canada.

The **Great Lakes** have a significant impact on the regional climate of the upper Midwest. They include Lake Superior, Lake Michigan, Lake Huron, Lake Erie, and Lake Ontario. All the Great Lakes except Lake Michigan are shared between the United States and Canada. Winds that cross the lakes pick up moisture, which increases precipitation (including snowfall) on the eastern side of each lake. The lakes also have more moderate air temperatures than the surrounding land (similar to the oceans), which makes for longer growing seasons on lands that border the eastern sides. As a result, the Niagara Peninsula is the major fruit-growing region in Canada[5]

Dry climates dominate in the Great Plains, the Intermountain West, and the Southwest U.S. These areas have semi-desert to desert conditions, with less than 20 inches of annual precipitation. The dry conditions support only short grasses and desert shrubs. Phoenix, Las Vegas, and Salt Lake City are examples.

Rainfall tends to decrease with westward travel from the Atlantic coast. Most of the East travel receives 40–80 inches; the central area receives 20–40 inches; the Great Plains receive 10–20 inches; and the Southwest deserts receive less than 10 inches. The main exception is the Northwest Pacific coast, which has a very mild and very wet climate.[6]

The polar climate dominates past the boreal forests in the far northern edges of Alaska and Canada. Hawaii, which is part of Oceania region, is dominated by the humid equatorial (tropical) climate.

The variety of climate regions represented across North America that the region has numerous natural disasters on what seems like a regular basis. Heat waves, droughts, floods, wildfires, extreme winter storms, tornadoes, hurricanes, and tropical storms are all common and often follow the calendar each year.

Tornadoes

Typically, tornadoes occur in the middle latitudes. They are prevalent across all continents, but North America, Europe, and Australia are the most common, sites. Antarctica is the only continent in which tornadoes are not found.

Beautiful defined tornado in American Plains

Rain Shadow Effect

The side of mountains that directly faces oncoming air is the windward side. On the windward side air rises and cools, leading to wet conditions. The side of mountains opposite the flow of oncoming air is the leeward side. Air descends, warms, and dries out on the leeward side. The rain shadow effect refers to the warm and dry air on the leeward side of mountains. Given the north to south orientation of U.S. and Canadian mountains, the west side tends to be the windward side; the east side tends to be the leeward side.[7]

Humid East versus Dry West

The **100th meridian** (line of 100 degrees west longitude) is a significant boundary line for Canada and the United States, separating humid conditions on the east from dry conditions on the west.[8] The **Mississippi River**, the predominat river in the United States, lies just east of the 100th meridian and can be designated as the key physical feature that separates the dry and humid areas, as well.

The **Dry West is** located west of the 100th meridian, averages generally less than 20 inches of annual precipitation, includes mostly short grasses and desert shrubs, has a browner landscape, and has a sparser and more scattered population.

The **Humid East** is located east of the 100th meridian, averages more than 20 inches of annual precipitation, includes mostly tall grasses and forests, has a greener landscape, and has a more dense and concentrated population.[9]

Indigenous Americans

Evidence indicates that the first **Indigenous Americans** entered the Americas at a historic land connection known as the **Bering Land Bridge**, which connected Asia to Alaska. The Indigenous Americans came from northeast Asia and entered by this land bridge into central Alaska, which was an unglaciated area at the time. Material (fossil) evidence and nonmaterial (language) evidence indicates the time of their arrival.[10] Many people settled in the lands of North America, but others migrated to the regions of Middle America and South America.

The Indigenous Americans had a similar ecological philosophy to most Asians—a respect for the environment and a desire to maintain harmony and balance with the environment. Thus, few changes were made in the physical environment.[11] This desire is still very alive today, where many indigenous groups have stood up against environment destruction of their lands.

In the east, Indigenous Americans were mainly farmers who needed to clear the forests for fields and settlements. They used a **slash-and-burn** method to cut and burn the forests, creating old fields or open areas within the forest. In the central areas, slash-and-burn farming changed former natural forest areas into tall, lush prairie grasses. The Indigenous Americans used natural features of the landscape to create odd-shaped, irregular plots of land using **metes and bounds**. Their trails followed the irregular

Burnaby, BC/Canada – Kwekwecnewtxw protect the Inlet March against the Trans Mountain expansion pipeline owned by the Canadian government. (March 2018)

field boundaries, creating a curving, irregular set of pathways. Only a few animals (turkey, guinea pig, llama, and alpaca) were bred for human survival purposes. Many crops originated with the Indigenous Americans—maize (corn), tobacco, squash, beans, tomato, potato, and pineapple. The most visible impact of the Indigenous Americans are in place names or **toponyms**. Chesapeake, Potomac, Patapsco, Patuxent, Mississippi, Missouri, Utah, and Dakota are good examples.[12]

European Arrival and Impacts

Written evidence indicates that Irish missionaries were the first Europeans to arrive in the Americas, as early as 700 AD. They were few in number and made no lasting impact. Scandinavians arrived by 1000 AD in larger numbers and left behind the oldest European settlement in the Americas, L'Anse Aux Meadows, on the island of Newfoundland. The year 1492 represents not the first European contact but the beginning of major European settlement and influence of the region.

Similar to Indigenous Americans, a major landscape impact by the Europeans was in the form of toponyms—Maryland, Virginia, Baltimore, Annapolis, New Orleans, Los Angeles, San Francisco, New York, New Jersey, Bronx, and Yonkers are a few examples. The Europeans had a different ecological philosophy than the Indigenous Americans. Most Europeans believed that the environment was there to be used to the maximum effect possible. Thus, in a few centuries, Europeans made extensive changes to the physical environment. The Europeans also brought many new infectious diseases that led to a rapid decline in many of the Indigenous American.[13]

Population Distribution and Change

The 365 million people in the United States and Canada region are unevenly distributed. Most of the U.S. population occupies the humid East and the far western edge while most of Canada's population is in the warmer, southern portion (most within 100 miles of the U.S. border).

At the beginning of the twentieth century, most North Americans lived in the Midwest and South census regions, with the smallest number occurring in the West census region. By the early twenty-first century, the South census region was the most populated, with the West becoming second most popu-

North America from space at night with city lights showing human activity in United States, Canada and Mexico.

lated. These changes are the result of internal population movements from east to west, north to south, and rural to urban.[14]

The main four periods of immigration for the Canada and the United States were 1600 to 1800, 1800 to 1890, 1890 to 1914, and post-1950. The 1600–1800s were a slower immigration period and consisted mainly of people from the British Isles and western European countries and Africans who came involuntarily to the region.

From 1800 to 1890, most migrants were European and overwhelmingly from northern and western Europe—British, German, and Scandinavian. Thus, most migrants were white, Anglo-Saxon, Protestants, and linguistically, religiously, and physically similar people.

The period of 1890–1914 experienced the greatest migration numbers in U.S. history, as was 1908–1912 for Canada. Over twenty-seven million Europeans migrated to the United States and Canada, most of them from south-

Newly arrived European immigrants at Ellis Island in 1921–21.

ern and eastern Europe—Italians, Poles, Czechs, and Slovaks are principal examples. This newer group was physically, linguistically, and religiously different from the earlier migrants. Intense ethnic and religious discrimination occurred against these "foreigners."

From 1914–1950, World War I, the Great Depression, World War II, and European recovery halted most European migration to North America.

Since 1950, the pace of migration quickened, but the sources became quite different. Currently, the rate of migration is similar to the pace from the late 1800s to early 1910s. Europe ceased to be a major source area and was replaced by Latin America (Mexico, Central America, and the Caribbean) and Asia (Philippines, Vietnam, China, and India are main sources).[15]

The diverse population across North America represents only 5 percent of the total world's population today. This region sits at a Stage 4 in the demographic transition model and has a 1.6 and 1.8 total fertility rate (TFR) for Canada and the United States, respectively, which is below replacement level.

Religious Regions

North America has three major religious regions: Roman Catholic Protestant, and Mormon.

The Roman Catholic religious' region in the USA includes two widely separated areas: the Northeast and the Southwest. Originally, the Northeast was a Protestant Christian area, but Irish migration and then larger numbers of Italians and eastern Europeans arrived. This resulted in the Northeast's becoming a Catholic-dominated area. Spanish missionaries and explorers introduced Catholicism to the Southwest in the 1500s and 1600s. More recently, huge numbers of Mexicans have intensified the Catholic dominance in the Southwest.

Protestant digions include baptists, Methodists, and Lutherans. The Baptist religious region includes most of the Southeast United States. British migrants introduced Baptist Protestantism. Baptist missionaries on horseback rapidly spread this denomination throughout the South. The Lutheran religious region includes most of the northern Great Plains and upper Midwest (Dakotas, Minnesota, Iowa, and Wisconsin). Migrants from northern Germany and Scandinavia introduced Lutheranism into this area.

The Methodist religious region extends from Maryland westward into the central Midwest. British migrants introduced Methodist Protestantism into central Maryland and it then spread directly westward. The Mormon religious region includes the Intermountain West

The Salt Lake Temple (Mormon Temple) is located in Salt Lake City Utah, America.

(the area between the Rockies and the Sierra-Cascades). The Church of Jesus Christ of Latter Day Saints (the LDS or Mormon religion) originated in upstate New York in 1830. The Mormons migrated to the Utah area in the late 1840s and rapidly spread their influence throughout most of the Intermountain West, even into the prairie provinces of Canada. Though they are Christian, they do not belong to the Catholic, Protestant, or Orthodox branches.[16]

Canada's population lives mainly near the southern border. It also has been influenced by migrating groups who carried their universalizing religions throughout its land. Roman Catholicism, has the largest number of adherents, with Protestant denominations making up the second largest religious groups.

Both countries have small population clusters of Jews, Muslims, Hindus, Sikhs, and Buddhists as well, as other religious adherents due to their pluralistic diverse society.

Racial and Ethnic Groups

At the end of the twentieth century, the major ethnic group was non-Hispanic White for both countries. The largest minority group was African Americans in the USA and Asians in Canada. Since the 2000 census, the Hispanic

UNITED STATES - CIRCA 1984 postage stamp.

hispanics live in the Southwest

population has become the largest minority group in the USA. It is estimated that, by 2050, the non-Hispanic White population will be a slight majority in the USA, followed up by Hispanic-White, Black, Asians and Indigenous Americans.[17]

Minority Group Patterns of the United States

The **Hispanic** population is now the largest minority group. Hispanics are a very diverse ethnic group. The largest Hispanic group is Mexican, which dominates in the U.S. Southwest. The Cuban group dominates in south Florida. The Puerto Rican group is dominant in the New York City area. New Mexico has the highest proportion of its population that is Hispanic. California has the largest number of Hispanics.

Southeast The **African American** population dominates in the Southeast U.S. Most of this group is descended from slaves brought to the Southeast to work on plantations. Mississippi has the highest proportion of its population that is African American. New York State has the largest number of African American.

The **Asian** population is mainly evident in the Pacific coast area. The Asians are another very diverse group, Chinese, Filipinos, Vietnamese, and Asian Indians are examples. Hawaii has the highest proportion of its population that is Asian. California has the largest number of Asians.

The Indigenous American population is mainly found in the Western U.S. The major area of dominance is the Four Corners area (where Utah, Arizona, Colorado, and New Mexico meet). Navajo, Hopi, Zuni, and Ute groups are concentrated in this area. Alaska has the highest proportion of its population that is Indigenous. California has the largest number of Indigenous Americans.[18]

Economic Changes and Patterns

Until the late 1800s, North America was mainly an agricultural economy. Beginning in the late 1800s, Canada and the USA shifted toward industrial economies. By 1950, they had become **post-industrial economies**, mainly comprised of marketing and service activities. The largest industries in Canada reside in the service sector, but the mining and lumber opportunities across the Canada and the tar sands of Alberta are nonetheless important.

The **North American Manufacturing Belt** is a large rectangular-shaped area that extends from Quebec in the Northeast down to Baltimore on the Southeast to St. Louis on the Southwest to Milwaukee on the Northwest, where the greatest concentration of industrial activity occurs. Over time, regional specializations developed—automobiles in the Detroit area; steel in the Pittsburgh-Chicago area; beer in the Milwaukee and St. Louis areas; finance, garment, and publishing in New York City.

Several agricultural regions still exist in the United States. Cotton

Wheat field; ears of golden wheat.

and tobacco dominate in the southeast. A **Dairy Belt** dominates in the Northeast and Great Lakes areas. The **Corn Belt** is a collection of corn, soybeans, cattle, and hogs that dominate in the central area, especially Illinois and Iowa. The **Wheat Belt** dominates in the Great Plains. **Truck farming** (fresh vegetables and fruits transported to nearby large urban areas) dominates along the Middle Atlantic coast from Virginia to Long Island.[19]

The North American Subregions

North America consists of three subregions: Greenland, Canada, and the United States.

Greenland

Greenland is the world's largest island, located off the northeast coast of Canada.[20] It still has ties as a constituent country to Denmark, so it is not technically an independent country. It sits high in the North Atlantic Ocean and has ice covering 80 percent of its **topography**, which is the physical or natural features of land. Greenland is the world's second largest ice sheet, and its polar climate dominates with cold temperatures for most of the year, although summer tem-

Kulusuk village, east Greenland

peratures can reach nearly 50°F. Greenland has impenetrable ice cap, though it, too, is warming in recent years, with the population occupying the green coastal zones.

The population of 56,600 people live in small coastal settlements. Their culture is similar to the Inuit people found across northern Canada. Their livelihood is tied to fishing, hunting, mining, and subsidies from Denmark. The Aurora Borealis' natural lightshow and the spectacular mammals are key attractions.

Canada

Canada is divided into ten provinces and three territories, all of which are situated in the region of North America but can act as subregions. The **maritime provinces** include Newfoundland and Labrador, Nova Scotia, Prince Edward Island, and New Brunswick. The **core provinces**, in terms of area and population, are Quebec and Ontario, situated in the central to eastern area, and British Columbia, situated on the far western edge. The **prairie provinces** of Manitoba, Saskatchewan, and Alberta are the last three of the ten provinces. The **Canadian territories** that are spread across northern Canada are Nunavut, the Northwest Territories, and the Yukon.

canada is #1 in oil reserve

The United States

The USA is comprised of 50 states but also includes several island territories that are not in the geographic region, but are politically connected to the USA. Guam, the Northern Mariana Islands, and America Samoa are part of the Oceania region. Puerto Rico and the US Virgin Islands are part of the Middle America region in the West Indies.

Most geographers break up the states by functions. The functional state subregions of the United States are as follows:

- **New England** (Maine, New Hampshire, Vermont, Massachusetts, Connecticut, and Rhode Island)
- **Mid-Atlantic** (New York, New Jersey, Pennsylvania, Maryland, and Delaware)
- **The South** (Virginia, West Virginia, North Carolina, South Carolina, Georgia, Florida, Alabama, Mississippi, Louisiana, Arkansas, Tennessee, and Kentucky)
- **Midwest** (Ohio, Indiana, Illinois, Michigan, Wisconsin, Minnesota, North Dakota, South Dakota, Iowa, Missouri, Nebraska, and Kansas)
- **Southwest** (Oklahoma, Texas, New Mexico, and Arizona)
- **The West** (Nevada, California, Utah, Colorado, Wyoming, Montana, Idaho, Oregon, Washington, Alaska, and Hawaii)

Review Terms

100th meridian	Hispanic	post-industrial economics
Asian	Humid East	prairie provinces
Aurora	Indigenous American	slash-and-burn
Bering Land Bridge	maritime provinces	Southwest
African American	metes and bounds	The South
Canadian territories	Mid-Atlantic	The West
core provinces	Midwest	topography
Corn Belt	Mississippi River	toponyms
Dairy Belt	New England	truck farming
Dry West	North America	Wheat Belt
federal state	North American	
Great Lakes	Manufacturing Belt	

Research Topics

look over all of this to study

acculturation - *your culture has been replaced another culture*
boreal forest - *coniferous trees needless, evergreen, or pintrees*
break-of-bulk point - *the ports, where they transport goods*
central business district (CBD) - *downtown cities where businesses are*
cultural assimilation - *you embrace another culture*
estuary -
fracking -

gentrification - *specific blight neighborhood, and revive the city*

green revolution - *agriculture revolution where they mix crops and grains*

megalopolis

Spanglish

tar sands

tundra

Credits

1. **Source:** From Thomas J. Karwoski, *World Regional Geography: An Introduction,* 1st ed., Copyright © 2016 by Kendall Hunt Publishing Company. Reprinted by permission.
2. **Source:** From Thomas J. Karwoski, *World Regional Geography: An Introduction,* 1st ed., Copyright © 2016 by Kendall Hunt Publishing Company. Reprinted by permission.
3. **Source:** From Thomas J. Karwoski, *World Regional Geography: An Introduction,* 1st ed., Copyright © 2016 by Kendall Hunt Publishing Company. Reprinted by permission.
4. **Source:** From Alan A. Lew, C. Michael Hall, and Dallen J. Timothy, *World Regional Geography: Human Mobilities, Tourism, Destinations, Sustainable Environments,* 2nd ed., Copyright © 2015 by Kendall Hunt Publishing Company. Reprinted by permission.
5. **Source:** From Alan A. Lew, C. Michael Hall, and Dallen J. Timothy, *World Regional Geography: Human Mobilities, Tourism, Destinations, Sustainable Environments,* 2nd ed., Copyright © 2015 by Kendall Hunt Publishing Company. Reprinted by permission.
6. **Source:** From Thomas J. Karwoski, *World Regional Geography: An Introduction,* 1st ed., Copyright © 2016 by Kendall Hunt Publishing Company. Reprinted by permission.
7. **Source:** From Thomas J. Karwoski, *World Regional Geography: An Introduction,* 1st ed., Copyright © 2016 by Kendall Hunt Publishing Company. Reprinted by permission.
8. **Source:** From Thomas J. Karwoski, *World Regional Geography: An Introduction,* 1st ed., Copyright © 2016 by Kendall Hunt Publishing Company. Reprinted by permission.
9. **Source:** From Thomas J. Karwoski, *World Regional Geography: An Introduction,* 1st ed., Copyright © 2016 by Kendall Hunt Publishing Company. Reprinted by permission.
10. **Source:** From Thomas J. Karwoski, *World Regional Geography: An Introduction,* 1st ed., Copyright © 2016 by Kendall Hunt Publishing Company. Reprinted by permission.
11. **Source:** From Thomas J. Karwoski, *World Regional Geography: An Introduction,* 1st ed., Copyright © 2016 by Kendall Hunt Publishing Company. Reprinted by permission.
12. **Source:** From Thomas J. Karwoski, *World Regional Geography: An Introduction,* 1st ed., Copyright © 2016 by Kendall Hunt Publishing Company. Reprinted by permission.
13. **Source:** From Thomas J. Karwoski, *World Regional Geography: An Introduction,* 1st ed., Copyright © 2016 by Kendall Hunt Publishing Company. Reprinted by permission.
14. **Source:** From Thomas J. Karwoski, *World Regional Geography: An Introduction,* 1st ed., Copyright © 2016 by Kendall Hunt Publishing Company. Reprinted by permission.
15. **Source:** From Thomas J. Karwoski, *World Regional Geography: An Introduction,* 1st ed., Copyright © 2016 by Kendall Hunt Publishing Company. Reprinted by permission.
16. **Source:** From Thomas J. Karwoski, *World Regional Geography: An Introduction,* 1st ed., Copyright © 2016 by Kendall Hunt Publishing Company. Reprinted by permission.
17. **Source:** From Thomas J. Karwoski, *World Regional Geography: An Introduction,* 1st ed., Copyright © 2016 by Kendall Hunt Publishing Company. Reprinted by permission.
18. **Source:** From Thomas J. Karwoski, *World Regional Geography: An Introduction,* 1st ed., Copyright © 2016 by Kendall Hunt Publishing Company. Reprinted by permission.
19. **Source:** From Thomas J. Karwoski, *World Regional Geography: An Introduction,* 1st ed., Copyright © 2016 by Kendall Hunt Publishing Company. Reprinted by permission.
20. **Source:** From Alan A. Lew, C. Michael Hall, and Dallen J. Timothy, *World Regional Geography: Human Mobilities, Tourism, Destinations, Sustainable Environments,* 2nd ed., Copyright © 2015 by Kendall Hunt Publishing Company. Reprinted by permission.

Chapter 3

MIDDLE AMERICA

No country should be left behind.

—Sebastian Pinera

Where Is Middle America?

Middle America consists of Mexico, Central America, and the West Indies, which are mainly composed of the Caribbean islands. Middle America resides in the Northern Hemisphere and refers to lands south of the North America region. It sits on the North America and the Caribbean tectonic plates but is also influenced by the minor Cocos and Nazca tectonic plates.

The Middle American region acts as a land bridge connecting North and South America.

© Peter Hermes Furian/Shutterstock.com

Major Qualities of Middle America

Middle America is physically and politically fragmented.[1] Physically, its mainland and fragmented islands connect the Americas and separate the Atlantic and Pacific Oceans. A narrow strip of land connecting two larger bodies of land is known as an **isthmus** as seen in the southern Central American countries of Costa Rica and Panama. Politically, the region is also fragmented with numerous states and territories belonging to the United Kingdom, the Netherlands, France, and the United States.

Middle America is culturally, racially, and ethnically diverse. There are several major groups that comprise the complex ethnic mosaic of this area. The approximate 220 million people who live in Middle America are mainly populated in one state: Mexico (132 million).

Middle America is a less-developed economic region, with widespread poverty, low incomes, and relatively rapid population growth. Recently, some economic reforms and increasing industrialization have occurred, especially in Mexico.[2]

Physical Geography

Middle America is comprised of a land bridge between North, South America, the **West Indies** (the two groups of Caribbean islands: the Greater Antilles and the Lesser Antilles), and the islands that make up the Lucayan Archipelago.

The **Greater Antilles** includes the four largest and most populated Caribbean islands: Cuba, Jamaica, Hispaniola, and Puerto Rico. The **Lesser Antilles** includes the smaller and less populated Caribbean islands.[3] The **Lucayan Archipelago** consists of the islands just north of the Caribbean and southeast of the United States. An **archipelago** is a chain or group of islands.

Middle America lies in the tropical and subtropical latitudes, with humid equatorial (tropical) climates predominating. The location is a major focus for hurricanes and geologic hazards. Middle America's location places it at the intersection of a number of major earth plates, including the Pacific Ring of Fire. Many earthquakes and volcanoes affect the Middle America region.[4]

Hurricanes

Starting in June each year, the collision of warm air masses off the coast of West Africa in the Atlantic Ocean gives rise to low pressure air systems that move toward the Caribbean Sea. About 100 of these swirls become tropical disturbances, and about a dozen of these become tropical storms. When the winds of these storms reach 74 miles per hour, they are classified as a **hurricane** on the **Saffir–Simpson**, which is a global hurricane wind scale that uses five categories of strength. (Hurricanes are also called typhoons and cyclones in other areas of the world.) When a hurricane hits land, it quickly loses its source of energy the warm waters of the tropical and subtropical ocean and seas and dies out, though winds can remain quite strong far inland. The hurricane season in the North Atlantic lasts through the end of November, when the warm air masses shift further southward.

Rock + H$_2$O + heat = decomposition of rocks

Hurricane Alley is the name given to the Caribbean region just north of the Great Antilles and up through the Gulf of Mexico. This area receives more tropical summer storms and hurricanes than anywhere else in the Americas. At least six hurricanes a year take this path, typically affecting the Yucatan Peninsula and making landfall in Texas or Louisiana, though they could also land in Mexico or Florida. Alternatively, some hurricanes approach North America to the north of the Greater Antilles and then

Hurricane approaching Texas in the Gulf of Mexico.

© Sasa Kadrijevic/Shutterstock.com

turn up the east coast of Florida, sometimes making landfall as far north as New York City or the New England states.

A large hurricane can have devastating impact on human settlements and the natural flora and fauna of the places in its path. Because of the nearness of South America to Africa, only the northernmost portions of that continent are ever affected by hurricanes (called cyclones in South America.) Hurricanes are also found in the Pacific Ocean side of North America, and, on rare occasions, they hit Hawaii and bring strong winds and rains to Baja, California, in Mexico and southern California.[5]

Major Altitude Zones

There are four major altitude zones in the mountainous areas of Middle America and South America: *tierra caliente, tierra templada, tierra fria*, and *tierra helada*. The **tierra caliente** is a hot and wet zone that occurs from sea level to about 3,000 feet. It is very warm and very wet, not climatically preferable for Europeans. This is a zone of tropical plantation agriculture, including sugar, bananas, rice, and other tropical crops.

The **tierra templada** is a temperate zone reaching to 6,000 feet. Latin America's largest population concentrations occur in this intermediate area. Grain crops, such as maize (corn), wheat, and many vegetables, are grown in this zone, as well as commercial coffee production.

The **tierra fria** is a cold area extending to 12,000 feet. Crops like potatoes and barley dominate in this zone. The **tierra helada** is the fourth altitude zone, extending to 15,000 feet. This altitude is above the tree line and can support only sheep grazing and other livestock herding on a seasonal basis.[6]

Tropical Deforestation

A major environmental issue in Latin America is tropical deforestation. **Tropical deforestation** is a process of forest clearance, mainly resulting from human activity. The greatest degree of global tropical deforestation occurs in Middle America and South America.

There are multiple causes of tropical deforestation. Agriculture is one important factor. In order to plant and grow crops, tropical forests need to be cleared. The most common way of removing the trees is through a practice known as slash-and-burn agriculture, in which people slash the trees in one season and burn the debris in another season. Cattle grazing is a rapidly growing profit center in Middle America. Many tropical farmers are aware of a large market in the developed countries for beef. They can make more money

Deforestation from the logging of rain forest, causes great environmental destruction.

© Rich Carey/Shutterstock.com

grazing cattle than growing crops. However, trees still need to be removed for grazing to take place. In addition to farming and grazing, settlement of people in towns and villages requires forests to be cleared. Road construction also is an important cause of deforestation. The tropical forests include commercially valuable species such as rubber, mahogany, teak, and ebony. However, these tree species are intermixed with other trees. To obtain one rubber tree may require extensive clearing of many other trees. Logging activity has become a significant cause of tropical deforestation.

There are also multiple consequences of tropical deforestation. The biosphere is adversely affected. In addition to the loss of the trees, habitat for many animals and plants is reduced or lost, leading to the possible disappearance of the species themselves. With tree removal, much precipitation is no longer absorbed by tree roots and leaves, leading to increased water runoff and erosion of soil, which travels to streams and causes sedimentation. The fast runoff of water causes flooding, and the chemistry of the atmosphere also changes. With fewer trees, less oxygen is released, and more carbon dioxide remains in the atmosphere. The increase in atmospheric carbon dioxide intensifies greenhouse warming, which is also intensified by the burning of the trees and burning releases even more carbon dioxide. Increasing deforestation also allows more solar energy to reach the surface, leading to even more warming.[7] See additional information in Chapter 4.

Early Indian Civilizations and European Colonization

Middle America has two major pre-European Indigenous American groups the *Maya* and the *Aztecs*. These two civilizations include dense concentrations of people in cities with monumental architecture, early agriculture, mathematical concept of zero, architectural notion of the arch, and presence of writing.

The **culture hearth** (place of origin) of the **Maya**, the Indigenous Americans in the lowland tropics of southern Mexico's Yucatan Peninsula, Guatemala, Belize, and Honduras reached its pinnacle from the third to the tenth centuries AD.[8] Remnants of the Mayan Civilization are prominent to this day on Mexico's Yucatan Peninsula and in the southern Mexican state of Chiapas, as well as in Guatemala and Belize. Indigenous communities abound in the Oaxaca area and in the remote Sierra Madre del Sur mountains (one of the three major mountain chains in Mexico) south of Mexico City.[9]

The culture hearth of the **Aztecs**, the Indigenous Americans in the highland zone of central Mexico, lasted from the fourteenth century to the sixteenth century.[10] The Aztec cities demonstrated highly advanced architectural design, irrigation technology, and social organization. The Aztec's glorious city of Tenochtitlan, built on the islands in Lake Texcoco, was destroyed by the Spanish. Today the lake is gone, and the cities[11] foundation is today's Mexico City valley region.

Hernan Cortes landed in Mexico in 1517 and named it New Spain, claiming it for the country of Spain. Aztec emperor Montezuma II thought that Cortes was the god-king Quetzalcoatl. Cortes used this confusion to conquer the Aztecs. The Spanish brought smallpox and other diseases to Mexico, which killed up to 90 percent of the estimated 25 to 30 million Indigenous Americans who inhabited Mexico and Central America at that time.

Spain ruled Mexico declared independence from Spain, in 1810. After a long war, Maxcio finally gained full independence in 1821. At that time, all of the southwestern United States, from Texas to California, was part of Mexico. The growing United States migration into these areas prompted the U.S. government to try to purchase them from Mexico, which Mexico refused. The **Mexican-American War** (1846–1848) ensued, resulting in Mexico's loss of about a third of its territory to the United States.[12]

Mayan Ruins in the Riviera Maya.

© DC_Aperture/Shutterstock.com

Hernan Cortes, 1485–1547, was a Spanish conquistador who conquered Mexico for Spain. He was also the first governor of New Spain.

© Morphart Creation/Shutterstock.com

The Spanish were the dominant Europeans in the mainland area of Middle America. In the Caribbean, Spanish colonialism occurred in Cuba, Dominican Republic, and Puerto Rico. The British had extensive colonial holdings in the Bahamas and Caribbean, including Jamaica, British Virgin Islands, Grenada, Barbados, and Trinidad and Tobago. On the mainland, the British controlled the lands of British Honduras (now Belize). The French had colonial control in Caribbean states such as Haiti, Guadeloupe, and Martinique. The Dutch had colonial possessions in the Netherlands Antilles (Aruba, Bonaire, and Curacao). U.S. colonies included Puerto Rico and the U.S. Virgin Islands.[13]

Cultural and Racial Diversity

Five main cultural and racial groups comprise the population of Middle America. Indigenous Americans are the original occupants of Middle America. Today, they are dominant in southern Mexico, the Yucatan Peninsula, and Guatemala.

Spanish Europeans historically dominated in Mexico and most of Central America. In the Caribbean islands, there were a variety of European groups, including Spanish, French, British, and Dutch. Today, the country of Costa Rica is largely European.

Mestizos are a blended group, with mixtures of Indigenous and European ancestry. The mestizos dominate in Mexico and most of Central America. African slaves, through forced migration, were brought to the Caribbean islands and coastal areas of Central America to work on plantations. African culture permeates the Caribbean islands today.

Mulattos are a blended group, with mixtures of European and African ancestry. The mulattos dominate in the Caribbean islands and in the coastal parts of Central America.[14]

Haciendas and Plantations

Haciendas are land use systems of large landholding units owned by a few wealthy individuals. Most of the people who work on the haciendas are peasants. The Spanish introduced this land system into the mainland area of Middle America. Haciendas use a mixed type of farming, with diversified crops grown for domestic use and extensive cattle grazing. It is not a very efficient system, and is primarily based on owning large areas of land with lots of cattle for social prestige purposes.

Courtyard of Hacienda Yaxcopoil, Mexico

© Zoltan.Benyei/Shutterstock.com

Bermuda

Bermuda is a mid-Atlantic island that is not part of the North America nor Middle America Regions. It is 620 miles off the coast of the United States. Bermuda is a territory of the United Kingdom but resembles the Caribbean in terms of agriculture, population, culture, and festivals.

It has a dark reputation for its surrounding area, called the **Bermuda Triangle.** Boats and planes are said to mysteriously disappear. Some say it is simply a highly traveled area, yet others cite magnetic changes within the earth and obscure levels of underwater gases as rationale.

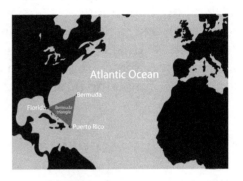

Bermuda Triangle.
© WindVector/Shutterstock.com

Plantations are land use systems of large landholdings owned by a few wealthy people Historically, most of the work was done by slaves, imported to work on the plantations. Northwest Europeans introduced this land system into the islands and Caribbean coastal parts of Central America. Plantations are a type of monoculture, where one cash crop is grown for export purposes. Commercial profit is the main purpose. Coffee, sugar, rice, and bananas are common plantation crops.[15]

A sugar plantation in Cuba showing the slave quarters on left, owner's house on center and sugar mill on right (1852).

© Everett Historical/Shutterstock.com

Mainland and Islands

One common way of dividing Middle America is by mainland and the islands. The mainland is comprised of Mexico and Central America. It is mainly a Euro-Indigenous area that employs the hacienda land use system. The Euro-African West Indies have an economy driven by the plantation land use system.[16]

The Pan-American Highway

In 1923, an agreement was reached by the Conference of American States to build a single transportation corridor (**Pan-American Highway**) that would link all of the Americas from Alaska in the north to Argentina and Chile in the south, some 16,000 miles. This goal has been met, except for a nearly 60-mile break in eastern Panama and northern Colombia, known as the **Darien Gap**. The Darien Gap is a swampy, rainforest-covered region with high biodiversity value that is under the control of dangerous drug smugglers and rebel guerrillas. The area's physical features have long prevented this last stretch of Interamericana from being developed, and, although adequate technology now exists to overcome these barriers, precarious security conditions continue to inhibit the project.[17]

The Middle America Region

Mexico

Mexico is the major country in Middle America. It has approximately 132 million people, over half of the region's total population. Mexico is the largest country in land area and the leading economic country within Middle America. Mexico's large land area provides many mineral resources, including oil, coal, natural gas, silver, iron, copper, and gold.

The core of Mexico extends from Veracruz on the Gulf of Mexico coast to Guadalajara on the west, with Mexico City in the middle. Mexico City is the largest city, political capital, and economic center of Mexico.[18] The northern Mexican states are the least populated, as is the southern portion of the **Baja Peninsula** that extends south of California and makes up the far northwest part of the country.

Mexico's southern region and the **Yucatán Peninsula** (the southern tail of Mexico that extends eastward into the Gulf of Mexico) include the country's largest concentration of Indigenous Americans. The southern region is economically poor with much political instability.

Pan-american highway

© Rainer Lesniewski/Shutterstock.com

MEXICO CITY, MEXICO (MAY 2013)

© Suriel Ramzal/Shutterstock.com

Maquiladoras are factories owned by foreign companies that are concentrated along the northern border with the U.S. They represent some of the fastest growing economic areas within Mexico. The incentive for the foreign companies is the attraction of cheap wage labor.

NAFTA (North American Free Trade Agreement) went into effect in 1994 but was rewritten in 2018. It established a free trade agreement among Canada, the United States, and Mexico that was intended to allow the easy movement of goods throughout these three countries. It has benefited Mexico, leading to U.S. factories' relocating to Mexico for its cheaper labor costs. This has resulted in a greater loss of U.S. jobs to Mexico. U.S. labor unions have greatly opposed the agreement. Many environmental organizations have also opposed it, due to the lack of pollution laws and regulations in Mexico.[19]

Central America

Central America includes the seven mainland countries between Mexico to the north and Colombia to the south. These countries include *Guatemala, Belize, Honduras, El Salvador, Nicaragua, Costa Rica,* and *Panama.* Spanish is the main language in these countries, due to colonization that occurred for 300 years in the region.

Guatemala is the only predominantly Indigenous American country in Central America. It is economically poor and politically unstable,[20] and, like El Salvador, has coastline only on the Pacific Ocean.

Belize has only coastline on the Caribbean Sea[21] and was a British colony until 1981. It is the only country in Central America that uses English as its official language and the largest coral reef system in the Western Hemisphere.

Honduras and Nicaragua are both recognized for the land bump that extends further into the Caribbean Sea than their neighboring Central American countries. These two countries are the poorest in Central America.

Costa Rica is a political democracy, a rarity in Central America. It has almost a purely European population, with higher levels of economic development relative to the rest of the sub region. It has no standing army and a large proportion of its territory is devoted to national parks. Costa Rica is globally known for its ecotourism industry.

Ecotourism is the process by which a country uses its natural ecology as a tourist draw. Costa Rica dedicates a high percentage of its budget to creating and maintaining ecological areas to attract tourists.[22]

An aerial view of the coral reef and deep cave that make up the famous diving spot of the Blue Hole in the Caribbean Ocean off the coast of Belize.

© Tami Freed/Shutterstock.com

Sky Walk Bridge in the Monteverde Rainforest of Costa Rica.

© Simon Dannhauer/Shutterstock.com

Queen Victoria navigating the Panama Canal; classified as a "Panamax" vessel, the largest the canal can accommodate.

© Fotos593/Shutterstock.com

Panama is the southernmost country in Central America. It has the highest level of rainforest cover of 40 percent, and it is dotted with amazing volcanoes. These forest and mountain regions are home to a vast array of flora and fauna. The **Panama Canal** was built by the French and Americans in the early twentieth century.[23] It connected the Atlantic and Pacific Oceans by removing the land that sat in the narrowest isthmus of Panama, as well as many lakes already in the area, reducing the need for ships to go to the tip of South America to reach the adjacent ocean. It is estimated that more than 14,000 ships pass through the canal each year,[24] which was expanded in the 2016 for even larger shipping vessels.

Havana, Cuba downtown skyline.

© Sean Pavone/Shutterstock.com

The West Indies

The West Indies includes the Lucayan Archipelago islands of the Bahamas, the Turks and Caicos islands (an overseas territory of the United Kingdom), and the two sets of Caribbean islands: the Greater and Lesser Antilles.[25]

The Greater Antilles are the four largest and most populated islands—Cuba, Jamaica, Hispaniola, Puerto Rico, plus the little Cayman Islands that remain territory of the United Kingdom. Cuba is the largest and most populated Caribbean country. It was a longtime Spanish colony before its independence. Since the late 1950s, it was controlled by a

Soufrière Hills

Montserrat's volcano, known as the Soufrière Hills, became active in 1995, after being dormant for centuries. Eruptions over the last 25 years destroyed parts of the island including the airport and docks around Plymouth, the island's historic capital. The southern end of the 39-square mile island is now part of an exclusion zone that is off limits for travel or habitation, and many residents have been forced to leave their homes due to the unpredictable behaviour of the volcano.

Active volcano in Montserrat with a large ash cloud.

© IndustryAndTravel/Shutterstock.com

Communist government led by the Castro brothers, Fidel and then Raul.[26] Today, Raul Castro has the highest authority in the country, with the president being second in command under him. Prior to succumbing to communist control, Cuba's capital city, Havana, was known as the **Paris of the Caribbean**, due to its cultural influence.

Jamaica, to the south of Cuba, is a former British colony.[27] Like most Caribbean islands, it is primarily African in origin, reflecting the former thriving slave trade on the island and in the region. Jamaica's slavery took place mostly on sugarcane plantations, but, with the abolition of slavery in 1834, the slaves were freed, and many became small-scale farmers.[28] It is known for its bauxite (aluminum ore) resources, as well as reggae music and Bob Marley.[29] The monotheistic religion of **Rastafarianism** was also birthed in this island country, which prophesied a return of Africans to their native continent and having all that had been lost to them restored.

Hispaniola, to the east of Cuba, is an island now politically divided between Haiti on the west and Dominican Republic on the east. Haiti is a former French colony, known for historical dictatorships, extensive poverty, and low incomes. Haiti is the poorest economy in the Western Hemisphere. Much of the country has been heavily deforested, leading to mudslides. Haiti is also prone to earthquakes and hurricanes. The Dominican Republic is a former Spanish colony[30] and is the most popular tourist destination in the Caribbean, due to its idea climate and biodiversity.

Puerto Rico is located east of Hispaniola. It is the easternmost and smallest of the Greater Antilles. Puerto Rico was a Spanish colony until the end of the Spanish-American War in 1898, when it became an American colony. In 1948, Puerto Ricans elected their own governor. In a 1952 referendum, voters approved the creation of a Commonwealth associated with the U.S. Puerto Ricans are U.S. citizens but pay no federal taxes on local incomes. There are many tax incentives for mainland companies and annual subsidies from the U.S. government.[31]

The island of Hispaniola houses both Haiti and Dominican Republic with capitals Port-au-Prince and Santo Domingo, in the Caribbean island group.

© Peter Hermes Furian/Shutterstock.com

Saint Barthelemy in the Caribbean Sea. This view shows the bay and harbour of Gustavia with Fort Karl and the typical red roofs.

© Naeblys/Shutterstock.com

The Lesser Antilles boasts the smaller southern Caribbean islands, many of which are volcanic, and makes up *two arcs of islands* (windward and leeward islands) and the three ABC islands.

The northern arc of islands, known as the **leeward islands**, include the island states of Antigua-Barbuda, Saint Kitts-Nevis, and Guadeloupe; as well as the overseas territories of the United States (Virgin Islands); the United Kingdom (British Virgin Islands; Anguilla, Montserrat); France (Saint Martin, Saint Barthelemy, Guadeloupe islands); and the Netherlands (Sint Maarten, Saba, Sint Eustatius).

The southern arc of islands, the **Windward Islands**, include the island states of Dominica, Saint Lucia, Barbados, St. Vincent, the Grenadines, Grenada, and Trinidad and Tobago, and the overseas territory of France (Martinique). Trinidad and Tobago has over one million people, making it the most populated of the Lesser Antilles islands. The **ABC Islands** sit just north of South America's Venezuela. They are Aruba, Bonaire, and Curacao, and are all constituent countries of the Netherlands.

Pink flamingos in Aruba.

© Natalia Barsukova/Shutterstock.com

⌈Review Terms³²⌋

ABC Islands
archipelago
Aztecs
Baja Peninsula
Bermuda
Bermuda Triangle
Central America
culture hearth
Darien Gap
ecotourism
Greater Antilles
haciendas
Hernan Cortes
Hispaniola
hurricane

hurricane alley
isthmus
leeward islands
Lesser Antilles
Lucayan Archipelago
maquiladoras
Maya
Mestizos
Mexican-American War
Mexico
Middle America
Mulattos
North American Free Trade
  Agreement (NAFTA)
Panama Canal

Pan-American Highway
Paris of the Caribbean
plantations
Rastafarianism
Saffir-Simpson
tierra caliente
tierra fria
tierra helada
tierra templada
tropical deforestation
West Indies
windward islands
Yucatan Peninsula

Research Topics[33]

borderland
brain drain
brain gain
creolization
fair trade
indentured labor
isolated proximity
neocolonialism
offshore banking
remittances
transculturation

Credits

1. **Source:** From Thomas J. Karwoski, *World Regional Geography: An Introduction*, 1st ed., Copyright © 2016 by Kendall Hunt Publishing Company. Reprinted by permission.
2. **Source:** From Thomas J. Karwoski, *World Regional Geography: An Introduction*, 1st ed., Copyright © 2016 by Kendall Hunt Publishing Company. Reprinted by permission.
3. **Source:** From Thomas J. Karwoski, *World Regional Geography: An Introduction*, 1st ed., Copyright © 2016 by Kendall Hunt Publishing Company. Reprinted by permission.
4. **Source:** From Thomas J. Karwoski, *World Regional Geography: An Introduction*, 1st ed., Copyright © 2016 by Kendall Hunt Publishing Company. Reprinted by permission.
5. **Source:** From Alan A. Lew, C. Michael Hall, and Dallen J. Timothy, *World Regional Geography: Human Mobilities, Tourism, Destinations, Sustainable Environments*, 2nd ed., Copyright © 2015 by Kendall Hunt Publishing Company. Reprinted by permission.
6. **Source:** From Thomas J. Karwoski, *World Regional Geography: An Introduction*, 1st ed., Copyright © 2016 by Kendall Hunt Publishing Company. Reprinted by permission.
7. **Source:** From Thomas J. Karwoski, *World Regional Geography: An Introduction*, 1st ed., Copyright © 2016 by Kendall Hunt Publishing Company. Reprinted by permission.
8. **Source:** From Thomas J. Karwoski, *World Regional Geography: An Introduction*, 1st ed., Copyright © 2016 by Kendall Hunt Publishing Company. Reprinted by permission.
9. **Source:** From Alan A. Lew, C. Michael Hall, and Dallen J. Timothy, *World Regional Geography: Human Mobilities, Tourism, Destinations, Sustainable Environments*, 2nd ed., Copyright © 2015 by Kendall Hunt Publishing Company. Reprinted by permission.
10. **Source:** From Thomas J. Karwoski, *World Regional Geography: An Introduction*, 1st ed., Copyright © 2016 by Kendall Hunt Publishing Company. Reprinted by permission.
11. **Source:** From Alan A. Lew, C. Michael Hall, and Dallen J. Timothy, *World Regional Geography: Human Mobilities, Tourism, Destinations, Sustainable Environments*, 2nd ed., Copyright © 2015 by Kendall Hunt Publishing Company. Reprinted by permission.
12. **Source:** From Alan A. Lew, C. Michael Hall, and Dallen J. Timothy, *World Regional Geography: Human Mobilities, Tourism, Destinations, Sustainable Environments*, 2nd ed., Copyright © 2015 by Kendall Hunt Publishing Company. Reprinted by permission.
13. **Source:** From Thomas J. Karwoski, *World Regional Geography: An Introduction*, 1st ed., Copyright © 2016 by Kendall Hunt Publishing Company. Reprinted by permission.
14. **Source:** From Thomas J. Karwoski, *World Regional Geography: An Introduction*, 1st ed., Copyright © 2016 by Kendall Hunt Publishing Company. Reprinted by permission.
15. **Source:** From Thomas J. Karwoski, *World Regional Geography: An Introduction*, 1st ed., Copyright © 2016 by Kendall Hunt Publishing Company. Reprinted by permission.

16. **Source:** From Thomas J. Karwoski, *World Regional Geography: An Introduction*, 1st ed., Copyright © 2016 by Kendall Hunt Publishing Company. Reprinted by permission.

17. **Source:** From Alan A. Lew, C. Michael Hall, and Dallen J. Timothy, *World Regional Geography: Human Mobilities, Tourism, Destinations, Sustainable Environments*, 2nd ed., Copyright © 2015 by Kendall Hunt Publishing Company. Reprinted by permission.

18. **Source:** From Thomas J. Karwoski, *World Regional Geography: An Introduction*, 1st ed., Copyright © 2016 by Kendall Hunt Publishing Company. Reprinted by permission.

19. **Source:** From Thomas J. Karwoski, *World Regional Geography: An Introduction*, 1st ed., Copyright © 2016 by Kendall Hunt Publishing Company. Reprinted by permission.

20. **Source:** From Thomas J. Karwoski, *World Regional Geography: An Introduction*, 1st ed., Copyright © 2016 by Kendall Hunt Publishing Company. Reprinted by permission.

21. **Source:** From Thomas J. Karwoski, *World Regional Geography: An Introduction*, 1st ed., Copyright © 2016 by Kendall Hunt Publishing Company. Reprinted by permission.

22. **Source:** From Thomas J. Karwoski, *World Regional Geography: An Introduction*, 1st ed., Copyright © 2016 by Kendall Hunt Publishing Company. Reprinted by permission.

23. **Source:** From Alan A. Lew, C. Michael Hall, and Dallen J. Timothy, *World Regional Geography: Human Mobilities, Tourism, Destinations, Sustainable Environments*, 2nd ed., Copyright © 2015 by Kendall Hunt Publishing Company. Reprinted by permission.

24. **Source:** From Alan A. Lew, C. Michael Hall, and Dallen J. Timothy, *World Regional Geography: Human Mobilities, Tourism, Destinations, Sustainable Environments*, 2nd ed., Copyright © 2015 by Kendall Hunt Publishing Company. Reprinted by permission.

25. **Source:** From Thomas J. Karwoski, *World Regional Geography: An Introduction*, 1st ed., Copyright © 2016 by Kendall Hunt Publishing Company. Reprinted by permission.

26. **Source:** From Thomas J. Karwoski, *World Regional Geography: An Introduction*, 1st ed., Copyright © 2016 by Kendall Hunt Publishing Company. Reprinted by permission.

27. **Source:** From Thomas J. Karwoski, *World Regional Geography: An Introduction*, 1st ed., Copyright © 2016 by Kendall Hunt Publishing Company. Reprinted by permission.

28. **Source:** From Alan A. Lew, C. Michael Hall, and Dallen J. Timothy, *World Regional Geography: Human Mobilities, Tourism, Destinations, Sustainable Environments*, 2nd ed., Copyright © 2015 by Kendall Hunt Publishing Company. Reprinted by permission.

29. **Source:** From Thomas J. Karwoski, *World Regional Geography: An Introduction*, 1st ed., Copyright © 2016 by Kendall Hunt Publishing Company. Reprinted by permission.

30. **Source:** From Thomas J. Karwoski, *World Regional Geography: An Introduction*, 1st ed., Copyright © 2016 by Kendall Hunt Publishing Company. Reprinted by permission.

31. **Source:** From Thomas J. Karwoski, *World Regional Geography: An Introduction*, 1st ed., Copyright © 2016 by Kendall Hunt Publishing Company. Reprinted by permission.

32. **Source:** From Thomas J. Karwoski, *World Regional Geography: An Introduction*, 1st ed., Copyright © 2016 by Kendall Hunt Publishing Company. Reprinted by permission.

33. **Source:** From Thomas J. Karwoski, *World Regional Geography: An Introduction*, 1st ed., Copyright © 2016 by Kendall Hunt Publishing Company. Reprinted by permission.

Chapter 4

SOUTH AMERICA

Few romances can ever surpass that of the granite citadel on top of the beetling precipices of Machu Picchu, the crown of Inca Land.

—Hiram Bingham

Where Is South America?

South America consists of entire continent of South America, which is divided into four subregions: North, West, South, and Brazil. It refers to the lands south of Middle America and north of Antarctica. It resides entirely in the Western Hemisphere, but the equator splits the continent into both the Northern and the Southern Hemispheres. The continental land sits mostly on the South American tectonic plate, but the Nazca tectonic plate greatly impacts the western edge of the continent.

The South American Region.

© Pyty/Shutterstock.com

Major Qualities of South America

The Andes Mountains and the Amazon Basin span much of South America. Over 430 million people live in South America, with nearly half of the population in one state, Brazil.

South America is culturally, racially, and ethnically very diverse. The same five groups that comprise the population of Middle America also create a complex ethnic mosaic of this region.

South America is a less developed economic region with huge disparities between rich and poor, leading to much political and cultural instability. Urbanization is very high in South America, despite its being a less developed region.[1]

Physical Geography

The **Andes Mountains** are the longest continuous mountain range on the earth's surface. They extend north to south along the western edge of the continent. **Mount Aconcagua** lies in the southern part of the Andes along the border of Chile and Argentina. Mount Aconcagua is the highest peak in the Americas, taller than Mount Denali (also known as Mount McKinley) in Alaska. Within the central Andes, especially in Bolivia, is the **Altiplano**. The Altiplano refers to a series of mountain valleys in the Andes with a dense concentration of people and activity.

The Amazon River

The Amazon River is about 4,000 miles (6,400 km) long and contains 20 percent of all of the river waters of the world. Its outflow is ten times greater than that of the Mississippi River. It has more than 1,000 tributaries, several of which are over 1,000 miles long, and it can be as much as 20 miles wide in some spots during the rainy season.

The Amazon River, in South America is the largest river in the world by length and discharge water volume. It flows through Brazil, Peru, Bolivia, Colombia, Ecuador, Venezuela and Guyana.

© oscar garces/Shutterstock.com

The Brazilian Highlands are also known as the **Brazilian Plateau**, and they have an average elevation of about 3,000 feet, with their highest peaks being over 9,000 feet. These highlands cover about half of the country of Brazil, and most of the country's population resides on their Atlantic coastal edge.[2]

There are two main grassland environments in South America: the *llanos* and the *pampas*.

The **llanos** is a lowland grassy area astride the border of Colombia and Venezuela. The **pampas**, a lowland grassy area in eastern Argentina that extends into Uruguay, home to the gaucho (the Argentinian equivalent to the U.S. cowboy).

The **Amazon Basin** is an extensive tropical rainforest whose watershed occupies half the land area of South America. The world's largest area of tropical deforestation occurs in the Amazon Basin. The Amazon River is the world's largest river in terms of volume of water and size of watershed area.

Llanos de Cuiva, Antioquia, Colombia.

© Foto 4440/Shutterstock.com

Steers in the Pampas of Argentina

© s.tomas/Shutterstock.com

Two desert environments in South America are the Atacama Desert and Patagonia. The **Atacama Desert** is a tropical desert in northern Chile, and it is the driest desert in the world. A combination of a semi-permanent high pressure system a cold ocean current offshore a position on the leeward side of South America and a leeward location on the rain shadow side of the Andes lead to very dry conditions here. **Patagonia** is a middle latitude desert in southern Argentina on the rain shadow side of the Andes.[3]

Moon Valley (Valle de la Luna), Atacama Desert, Chile

© sunsinger/Shutterstock.com

The Incan Empire

The **Inca** were the major pre-European Indian group in South America,[4] and it is estimated that they were 10 to 20 million human inhabitants in South America. Up to 95 percent of the indigenous population died of diseases that arrived with the Spanish. This widespread population loss is known as **demographic collapse**.[5] Their culture hearth was concentrated in the Andean Altiplano in the area of Bolivia. Similar to the Aztecs and the Mayans, the Incas were an advanced civilization with monumental architecture, the mathematical concept of zero, and the architectural idea of the arch. A highly centralized state with

Los Cuernos rocks and Lake Pehoe in Torres del Paine National Park, Patagonia, Chile.

© Olga Danylenko/Shutterstock.com

rather impressive transportation networks, their peak occurred around 1300 AD.[6]

The Tordesillas Line[7]

The two powerful countries of Europe in the early 1500s were Spain and Portugal, the vanguard of European overseas colonial expansion. In 1494, the two countries signed the Treaty of Tordesillas, dividing the world in half between them on the **Tordesillas line**, drawn down the middle of the Atlantic Ocean. Spain received the western half, and Portugal took everything to the east. This line was intended to give all of the New World to Spain and all of the uncolonized Old World to Portugal. However, the line ended up giving a large chunk of South America to Portugal, which became the Portuguese colony of Brazil.

Machu Picchu showcases the Incan civilization in the 15th century.

© Ed Lim/Shutterstock.com

Spain and Portugal both had policies to keep out all other Europeans from their territories. It is estimated that fewer than 150,000 Spaniards actually migrated to South America. Up to one million Portuguese migrated to Brazil, drawn by the gold rush in the 1700s. Although their numbers were not large, the Spanish and Portuguese political and religious domination of the continent significantly influenced the culture that has developed in both South and Central America in modern times.[8]

Cultural and Racial Matrix

There are five main cultural/racial groups that comprise the population of South America: *Indigenous American, European, Mestizo, African, and Mulatto*. Today, the Indigenous Americans are concentrated in the Andean Mountains. Europeans live in the southern states of Chile, Argentina, Uruguay, and southern Brazil. Mestizo is the largest group in countries such as Brazil, Colombia, Venezuela, Peru, Ecuador, and Paraguay. African and Mulatto groups are mainly found in the coastal areas of northern South America and northeast Brazil,[9] due to the large numbers of African slaves who were brought by both the Portuguese and Spanish.[10]

Geography of Cocaine

The coca plant has been highly valued in South America for centuries. It is used in teas, as an herbal medicine, and for its stimulant properties. Most coca plant production occurs in Bolivia, Peru, and Colombia and is distributed to the U.S. via Mexico. Fifty percent of the cocaine reaches Mexico from South America along the Pacific coast, while 25 percent comes to Mexico overland from South America through Guatemala. Another 25 percent comes to Mexico from South America along the Gulf of Mexico coast. It is estimated that 90 percent of the cocaine enters the U.S. from Mexico. Inside Mexico, the cocaine is controlled by a series of drug cartels that control many areas of Mexico.[11]

Indigenous Bolivian woman chewing coca leaf.

© dani3315/Shutterstock.com

Biodiversity

South America has more animal and plant species than any other major region on the planet. Scientists believe Brazil contains 20 percent of the global species biodiversity, with over 50,000 known plant species and 10 percent of known animal species (excluding those in the oceans). Yasuni National Park in eastern Ecuador, part of the Amazon Basin, is believed to have the greatest biological diversity per hectare (equals 2.47 acres) on the earth. Researchers have documented 596 bird species; 150 amphibian species; 1,100 tree species (up to 655 species in a single hectare); over 200 mammal species; and 100,000 insect species. All of these are the highest numbers recorded anywhere in the world. The **Galapagos Islands** off the coast of Ecuador are also known for their prestigious ecotourism and biodiversity tours. Unfortunately, oil companies may threaten the biodiversity and indigenous tribal groups living in the area.[12]

Ecuador's Galapagos Islands are known for the Galapagos tortoises.

© FOTOGRIN/Shutterstock.com

Hoatzins in Yasuni National Park, Ecuador.

© almond/Shutterstock.com

The Latin American City

Urbanization rates are high in both Middle America and South America, a result of the Spanish and Portuguese influence of the Iberian Peninsula.

The spatial structure of the Latin American city is quite different than the North American city. In Latin America, the center of the city carries status and prestige. Wealthy groups concentrated near the center to take advantage of its proximity to cathedrals, palaces, and museums. The outskirts of the Latin American city are where most of the landless poor live in squatter settlements called **favelas**. In contrast, the North American poor minority groups are concentrated adjacent to the business district, with the middle and upper income groups found on the outskirts in suburban areas.[13]

Favellas in a poor neighborhood of Sao Paulo Brazil. (October 2018)

© Alf Ribeiro/Shutterstock.com

The South American Region

South America is comprised of four subregions: The North, The West, The South, and Brazil.

The North

The North region includes the countries of Colombia, Venezuela, and the Guianas. These countries are located on the Caribbean and Atlantic coast. Economically, these warm and wet tropical climates were conducive to early European plantation development. The general lack of Indigenous Americans led the Europeans to import forced laborers from Africa and Asia.

Colombia is the most populated country in The North subregion. It is mainly known for its production and export of coffee and cocaine. Colombian coffee is well known for its high quality. Cocaine production has been the basis for much of the violence and instability within Colombia over the last few decades.

Venezuela is economically known for its oil production and exports. In the late 1990s, Venezuela elected an anti-American, anti-free trade candidate, Hugo Chavez. Under Chavez and his successor, Venezuela has become an autocratic state with leftist tendencies that decimated the state and left it in the throes of an economic crisis.

The Guianas are three small, less populated countries along the northeast coast of South America: Guyana, Suriname, and French Guiana. Most of the people in the Guianas are African and mulatto. These are the only areas of South America that are neither Spanish nor Portuguese in language and settlement.

Guyana, rich in gold and oil, is a former British colony that once was known as British Guiana. English is still the official language. Guyana is most identified with the Jonestown Massacre in the late 1970s. Hundreds of members of an American religious cult died from mass suicide–murder under the leadership of a charismatic leader named Jim Jones.

Suriname is a former Dutch colony that used to be known as Dutch Guiana. Dutch is still the official language. Suriname includes relatively large Asian groups in its population. **Bauxite** (aluminum ore) and oil are important economic minerals. Both Guyana and Suriname have significant issues in terms of tropical deforestation.

French Guiana is South America's only dependency. It is officially a department of France, and French is the official language. Gold and fishing are traditional resources. The European Space Agency has a launch complex on the coast, which accounts for the majority of the economic activity now.[14]

Protest in Caracas, Venezuela against the government of Nicolas Maduro. (April 2017)

© Reynaldo Riobueno/Shutterstock.com

Tree roots in the French Guyana rainforest

© Deplanque Olivier/Shutterstock.com

The West

The West region is economically the poorest, least developed subregion of South America. The Andes Mountains topographically cover the area. Historically, the Indigenous Americans have been the main occupants of the land. The West includes the countries of Ecuador, Peru, Bolivia, and Paraguay.

Ecuador is the smallest of the Andean states. Its name comes from its location astride the equator. Guayaquil is the largest city, the commercial center, and the main port of Ecuador. The capital is Quito in the Andean mountains. Oil is the main export, with bananas being a traditional plantation crop.

Peru is the largest country in area and population within The West subregion. Peru has an extensive set of mineral resources, including copper, lead, and gold. Recent oil and natural gas discoveries in the East may help to stimulate development of this part of the country. Peru is most known for Machu Picchu, one of the best pre-European sites in South America. Near Cuzco, it was part of the hearth area of the Incan Empire.

Bolivia is one of *two landlocked states* in South America. It has been a major producer of coca and cocaine that is eventually transported to Mexico and the U.S. There is a significant European and Indigenous American divide within Bolivia. The western mountainous part is inhabited by Indigenous Americans,

Monument Mitad del Mundo in Quito, Ecuador represents the equator's pathway.

© Fotos593/Shutterstock.com

Vinicunca, Peru - Rainbow Mountain (5200 m) in Andes.

© cge2010/Shutterstock.com

who make up the majority of the population. The coca producing areas are in the West, as well as Bolivia's two capitals. La Paz is the administrative capital, while Sucre is the judicial capital. The eastern lowlands are home to the Mestizo minority, who actively seek more autonomy for their part of the country. Most of the mineral resources are in the East.[15]

Paraguay is the other landlocked state in South America. Its livelihood comes mainly from agriculture, with the soybean crop's being especially important. The country is split into two topographic designations of east and west and two corresponding climates of tropical and subtropical. The environment is clean, due to the use of hydroelectricity, but land reform is needed. Nearly half the population lives in poverty that impacts the Indigenous Americans most directly.

The South

The South region is the only middle latitude part of South America. It is comprised of the largest proportions of Europeans in the continent. The South includes three countries: Argentina, Chile, and Uruguay.

Argentina has the largest population and land area of The South subregion. It is one of the most urbanized countries in the world; over 90 percent of the population lives in urban areas. Buenos Aires is a classic example of a primate city: it is the largest city, the political capital, and the economic center of the country. Argentina is a major exporter of beef and wheat, and considers itself to be the most sophisticated state in South America. Nevertheless, Argentina did go through a turbulent period known as "The

Dirty War" (mid-1970s to mid-1980s). A repressive military junta led to the disappearance of tens of thousands of young people and launched a failed invasion of the British-held Falkland Islands.[16] There are still issues today with the **Falkland Islands** or the *Las Malvinas*, as the Argentines call them. The British still control the islands to the east of southern Argentina and are unlikely to give up control, due to the oil found there.

Chile is an elongated state that extends over 2,500 miles north to south. This extended latitude location provides dramatic differences in climate, from the Atacama Desert in the north to a Mediterranean-type climate in the middle to a Marine climate in the south. Overwhelmingly, most of the population is concentrated in the milder central area, including the capital and largest city of Santiago. Fruit, wine, and vegetables are main exports from the central area. Copper is a main export from the northern Atacama Desert area. The world's largest open pit copper mine (the second deepest in the world)

Devil's Throat at the Iguazu Falls in Argentina and Brazil

© Donatas Dabravolskas/Shutterstock.com

Aerial view on skyscrapers of Financial District of Santiago, capital of Chile under early morning fog

© Marianna Ianovska/Shutterstock.com

is within this northern area. The southern area depends up on logging and timber as exports. Chile's agricultural economy benefits from its southern hemisphere location (Chile's summer season is the winter season for the U.S. and Europe). Chile also benefits from its access to the growing Pacific Rim economies. One major problem of the Pacific Ocean location is that Chile lies on the pacific Ring of Fire, as extensive major earthquakes often affect the Santiago area.

Uruguay is a small, low population state across the water from Buenos Aires in Argentina. Montevideo is another classic primate city. Uruguay acts as a buffer between Brazil to the north and Argentina to the south. Meat products and textiles are important exports.[17]

Brazil

Brazil is the major country in South America, containing half the land area and half the population. Approximately 212 million people in Brazil. The world's largest tropical rainforest, experiencing tremendous rates of **deforestation** lies within the vast Amazon Basin. Brazil has one of the most diverse populations in South America. It is a mixture of European, African, and Indigenous American peoples that blend into a composite Brazilian culture. Brazil is the only Portuguese speaking country in South America. A benefit of area size having the world's fifth largest land area is its vast array of minerals, including bauxite, iron, oil, and gas. Historically, Brazil had the greatest disparity in income between rich and poor in the world, a contrast vividly seen in photographs today.

Brazil's five areas include The *Northeast, The Southeast, Sao Paulo State, The South,* and *The Interior.* The Northeast area includes the cities of Salvador, Recife and Fortaleza. It is the country's culture hearth, the place of origin of Brazilian culture. The plantation economy dominated the Northeast area; it contains the greatest concentrations of African and mulatto groups. Today, it is economically poor and depressed, with extensive outmigration of people and activities toward the more populated and developed southern areas.

Rio de Janeiro with Christ the Redeemer standing at 38 m on Corcovado Mountain

© dmitry_islentev/Shutterstock.com

The Southeast area includes Rio de Janeiro, the cultural center and former political capital of Brazil. The Sao Paulo State area includes the city of Sao Paulo, the largest city in Brazil and South America. Sao Paulo is also one of the largest *megacities* (city with 10 million plus) in the world. Sao Paulo is the industrial center of Brazil. Its economy was initially stimulated by the success of coffee plantations (Brazil is first in world coffee production). Today orange juice concentrate (Brazil is first in world production) and soybeans (Brazil is second in world production) have become major economic leaders. Sao Paulo's population is a microcosm of Brazil: waves of Europeans (Portuguese, Italians, Germans, and British), Africans and mulattos from the Northeast area, and Japanese have created a rich urban tapestry. Today Sao Paulo has the largest concentration of Japanese outside of Japan.

The South area includes that part of Brazil south of Sao Paulo. It is the most European, most developed, and wealthiest part of Brazil. The Interior area includes the capital city of Brasilia. In 1960, Brazil built a modern, new city in the empty interior built to reduce congestion and overcrowding along the southeast coast. Brasilia is a classic example of a forward capital. The Amazon Basin comprises the majority of land in this area.[18]

Amazon River Snakes through the Amazon Rainforest in Brazil.

Impacts of Deforestation at the Brazilian Amazon Frontier

Amy Parsons, April 2019

IMPACTS OF DEFORESTATION AT THE BRAZILIAN AMAZON FRONTIER, APRIL 2019

Contributed by Amoreena Parsons. © Kendall Hunt Publishing Company

The Amazonian frontier is characterized by the area that has seen a dramatic transition in land cover over the past half-century. Specifically, in the area known as the "arc of deforestation," which has experienced over 80 percent of the cumulative and current effects of forest clearing to date. The peak rate of Brazilian Amazonian deforestation occurred in 2004 and did see a steady decline over the next few years. However, 2018 saw the largest rate of deforestation in a decade, solidifying the fact that the problem has not gone away and still poses a major threat to forests in the region. In the Brazilian Amazon, the large-scale shift to

(Continued)

mechanized agriculture, extensive logging, and intensive cattle ranching have led to a more vulnerable transitional ecosystem between moist, tropical forests and seasonally dry, savannah vegetation.

Impacts of disturbance

Increased rates of forest loss along the arc of deforestation have created a regional positive feedback cycle that is predicted to worsen in the coming decades. After forest is cleared, the surface albedo (or reflectivity) drastically increases allowing for a shift in the absorption of incoming solar radiation. In turn, the air above that land heats up faster than it would if the energy was being absorbed by dark tropical vegetation and draws away moisture, therefore lessening the amount of potential rainfall over forests. Along newly formed forest edges, the microclimate at the forest floor changes with increased amounts of incoming sunlight and wind, making normally moist conditions much drier.

Forest edges also see the mortality of large trees increase and an invasion of native and nonnative pioneer grasses resulting in a homogenous landscape and a decrease in overall biodiversity. As grasses take over a landscape, they create a blanket of available fuels, which typically burn at high intensities especially under extremely warm and dry conditions. These fire-favorable conditions are becoming more common thanks to anthropogenic climate change, which is increasing the length and severity of droughts. These conditions become exacerbated by a positive feedback cycle in which fires burn through these areas opening the canopy further, thus increasing the size of forest edges, which cause that forest to become more susceptible to burning. As a result, the arc of deforestation in Brazil is at the highest risk of fire due to the coalescence of compounded anthropogenic and environmental variables.

Solutions

With demands for a shift in land management practices at the Amazonian agricultural frontier, the general consensus seems to be a push for transforming the already cleared areas into ones that are higher-yielding but also maintained in a long-term, sustainable way. Other experts have recommended a change in economic markets and political drivers that influence forest degradation

Deforestation shows the logging environmental destruction of the rainforest.

© Rich Carey/Shutterstock.com

at the frontier boundary. Seemingly, simple solutions have emerged that directly call for harsher enforcement of already established environmental policies through mechanisms such as the Brazilian Forest Code. However, the Brazilian Forest Code has seen the removal of important regulations in 2018, making it easier for landowners to legally clear forests. Improvements to the general monitoring of annual forest degradation and newly established protected forests and indigenous preserves have begun to take effect on reducing the fire-related devastation to forests. However, emphasis on local education could be extremely beneficial in order to see longer-term changes to the way people are using their land. Overall, it will take a combined and extensive approach to ease the positive feedback cycle involving deforestation, agricultural intensification, pasture expansion, increased fire frequency, and climate change that has the potential to drive further degradation in other parts of the continent and possibly the globe.

Review Terms

altiplano
Amazon Basin
Amazon River
Andes Mountains
Atacama Desert
bauxite
Brazil
Brazilian Plateau

deforestation
demographic collapse
Falkland Islands
favelas
Galapagos Islands
Incallanos
Mount Aconcagua
pampas

Patagonia
South America
The Guianas
The North
The South
The West
Tordesillas Line

Research Topics

agrarian reform
Bolsa Familia
commercial agriculture
cultural pluralism
dependency theory
dollarization
el niño
floating islands
grassification
insurgent state
la niña
landlocked
neoliberalism
rural-to-urban migration
squatter settlement
uneven development

Credits

1. **Source:** From Thomas J. Karwoski, *World Regional Geography: An Introduction*, 1st ed., Copyright © 2016 by Kendall Hunt Publishing Company. Reprinted by permission.
2. **Source:** From Alan A. Lew, C. Michael Hall, and Dallen J. Timothy, *World Regional Geography: Human Mobilities, Tourism, Destinations, Sustainable Environments*, 2nd ed., Copyright © 2015 by Kendall Hunt Publishing Company. Reprinted by permission.
3. **Source:** From Thomas J. Karwoski, *World Regional Geography: An Introduction*, 1st ed., Copyright © 2016 by Kendall Hunt Publishing Company. Reprinted by permission.
4. **Source:** From Thomas J. Karwoski, *World Regional Geography: An Introduction*, 1st ed., Copyright © 2016 by Kendall Hunt Publishing Company. Reprinted by permission.Lew, Hall, and Timothy, *World Regional Geography Human Mobilities, Tourism Destinations, Sustainable Environments*, 2nd ed.
5. **Source:** From Alan A. Lew, C. Michael Hall, and Dallen J. Timothy, *World Regional Geography: Human Mobilities, Tourism, Destinations, Sustainable Environments*, 2nd ed., Copyright © 2015 by Kendall Hunt Publishing Company. Reprinted by permission.
6. **Source:** From Thomas J. Karwoski, *World Regional Geography: An Introduction*, 1st ed., Copyright © 2016 by Kendall Hunt Publishing Company. Reprinted by permission.
7. **Source:** From Thomas J. Karwoski, *World Regional Geography: An Introduction*, 1st ed., Copyright © 2016 by Kendall Hunt Publishing Company. Reprinted by permission.
8. **Source:** From Alan A. Lew, C. Michael Hall, and Dallen J. Timothy, *World Regional Geography: Human Mobilities, Tourism, Destinations, Sustainable Environments*, 2nd ed., Copyright © 2015 by Kendall Hunt Publishing Company. Reprinted by permission.
9. **Source:** From Thomas J. Karwoski, *World Regional Geography: An Introduction*, 1st ed., Copyright © 2016 by Kendall Hunt Publishing Company. Reprinted by permission.
10. **Source:** From Alan A. Lew, C. Michael Hall, and Dallen J. Timothy, *World Regional Geography: Human Mobilities, Tourism, Destinations, Sustainable Environments*, 2nd ed., Copyright © 2015 by Kendall Hunt Publishing Company. Reprinted by permission.
11. **Source:** From Thomas J. Karwoski, *World Regional Geography: An Introduction*, 1st ed., Copyright © 2016 by Kendall Hunt Publishing Company. Reprinted by permission.
12. **Source:** From Alan A. Lew, C. Michael Hall, and Dallen J. Timothy, *World Regional Geography: Human Mobilities, Tourism, Destinations, Sustainable Environments*, 2nd ed., Copyright © 2015 by Kendall Hunt Publishing Company. Reprinted by permission.
13. **Source:** From Thomas J. Karwoski, *World Regional Geography: An Introduction*, 1st ed., Copyright © 2016 by Kendall Hunt Publishing Company. Reprinted by permission.
14. **Source:** From Thomas J. Karwoski, *World Regional Geography: An Introduction*, 1st ed., Copyright © 2016 by Kendall Hunt Publishing Company. Reprinted by permission.
15. **Source:** From Thomas J. Karwoski, *World Regional Geography: An Introduction*, 1st ed., Copyright © 2016 by Kendall Hunt Publishing Company. Reprinted by permission.
16. **Source:** From Thomas J. Karwoski, *World Regional Geography: An Introduction*, 1st ed., Copyright © 2016 by Kendall Hunt Publishing Company. Reprinted by permission.
17. **Source:** From Thomas J. Karwoski, *World Regional Geography: An Introduction*, 1st ed., Copyright © 2016 by Kendall Hunt Publishing Company. Reprinted by permission.
18. **Source:** From Thomas J. Karwoski, *World Regional Geography: An Introduction*, 1st ed., Copyright © 2016 by Kendall Hunt Publishing Company. Reprinted by permission.
19. **Source:** From Alan A. Lew, C. Michael Hall, and Dallen J. Timothy, *World Regional Geography: Human Mobilities, Tourism, Destinations, Sustainable Environments*, 2nd ed., Copyright © 2015 by Kendall Hunt Publishing Company. Reprinted by permission.

Chapter 5

EUROPE

Someday, following the example of the United States of America, there will be a United States of Europe.

—George Washington

Where is Europe?

As a continent, Europe extends eastward from the Atlantic Ocean to the Ural Mountains in west central Russia, and it extends northward from the Mediterranean Sea to the Arctic Ocean. As a region, Europe extends eastward from the Atlantic Ocean to the western border of Russia. It includes nearly fifty countries from Iceland to the edge of Russia. It resides along the Prime Meridian, which separates it between the Western and Eastern Hemispheres, but it is entirely in the Northern hemisphere. Europe sits mainly on the Eurasian tectonic plate, although Iceland, Malta, and Cyprus share other tectonic plates.

Major Qualities of Europe

Europe is a highly developed world region. Densely populated with numerous political states, some states are large in area and population, such as Germany, France, and Italy. Other states are small in area and population, such as San Marino, Monaco, and Vatican City. Europe currently has about 743 million people who are highly urbanized with a largely aging, declining population. Historically, it has been a major center of innovation, with many significant developments (revolutions) originating in Europe and spreading throughout the rest of the world. Its continental land makes up a large **peninsula** (a landmass with water on three sides) and is often referred to as a "peninsula of peninsulas," as many of the smaller peninsulas (Balkan, Cotentin, Crimea, Iberian, Italian, and Jutland) extend from the larger.

The European Region has tremendous diversity.

© Pyty/Shutterstock.com

55

The largest rivers of Europe are the *Rhine, Danube,* and the *Volga* rivers. Smaller rivers are also very important, in this region, as well as several important canals, i.e., Mittelland Canal. The canals that combine the river systems of the Rhine and the Danube travel through ten different countries and provide a significant route for tour boats, canal barges, small cruise ships, and trading vessels.

Climate Patterns

The Europe region is mainly located in the middle latitude area of the world (30 degrees to 60 degrees North latitude). Most of western Europe has a humid temperate (mild) marine climate. Temperatures are moderate through the year, with 30–80 inches of

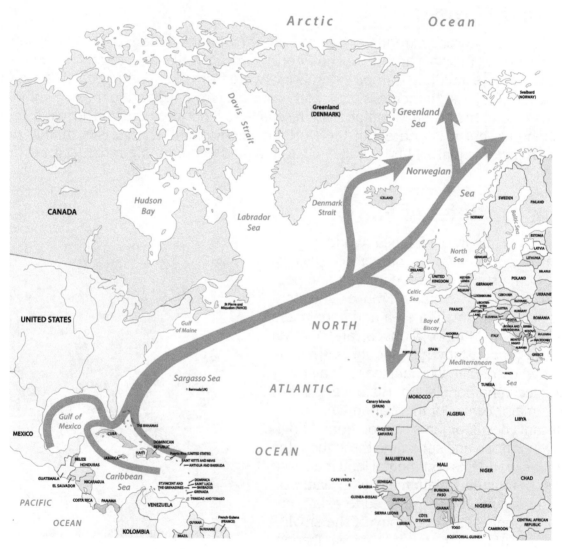

Map of the North Atlantic Gulf Stream in the North Atlantic Ocean

© Rainer Lesniewski/Shutterstock.com

annual precipitation. These mild and wet conditions are the result of the moderating effect of adjacent water bodies, as well as the North Atlantic Current (Drift). The **North Atlantic Current**, a warm ocean current originating in the tropics and moving northeast across the Atlantic Ocean, brings warm and wet weather to most of western Europe. London, Dublin, and Paris are examples.

Most of southern Europe has a humid temperate (mild) Mediterranean climate. Temperatures are mild through the year, with 15–30 inches of annual precipitation and a summer drought seasonal pattern. Rome and Athens are examples. Most of eastern and far northern Europe has a humid, cold climate. There are significant seasonal temperature changes with short, hot summers and long, cold winters. Precipitation averages about 20–40 inches annually. These climates are also known as continental climates, due to their[8] continental location away from large bodies of water. Stockholm, Helsinki, and Warsaw are examples.[9]

Landform Patterns

The Western Uplands largely comprise the western edge of Europe. These are hilly and highland areas, such as most of Scandinavia, western parts of the British Isles, Brittany peninsula in France, and the western Iberian Peninsula (Spain and Portugal).

The **Alpine System** comprises most of southern Europe. These are mountainous areas, including the Pyrenees along the Spain/France border, Alps in central Europe, Apennines in central Italy, Carpathians in eastern Europe, and the Balkan Peninsula.

The Central Uplands in central Europe are located to the north of the Alpine System. These are transitional, hilly areas at the northern edge of the Alpine System and include eastern France and central Germany.

The **North European Lowland** is the most significant landform region. This is the main lowland area of Europe, extending from western France through southern England, Belgium, Netherlands, Denmark, northern Germany, Poland, Ukraine, and into European Russia. It is a major historical route of movement from west to east. The North European Lowland includes most of Europe's population, large cities, agriculture, and industry.[10]

Jungfraujoch in the Swiss Alps.

© Edler von Rabenstein/Shutterstock.com

European Revolutions

Historically, Europe has been a major hearth of global innovations. The medieval agricultural revolution began around 1200–1400. Contour plowing, hybrid strains of grain, and land consolidation were hallmarks of this phenomenon. Developing technology and applying new scientific methods revolutionized farming and greatly improved crop yields.

A commercial revolution occurred from 1400–1700, based on maritime shipping and trade and coinciding with the age of European discovery and exploration. The **industrial revolution** started in northern England in the mid-1700s. It spread to mainland Europe and diffused globally through the migration of northern and western Europeans. In many ways, it is the uneven spread (diffusion) of the industrial revolution that resulted in the current global range of more developed and less developed countries. The industrial revolution involved the use of machines in factories; these machines allowed a more effective, efficient, and cheaper way to produce mass volumes of goods.

The modern urban revolution is closely related to the industrial revolution. As Europe began to industrialize, it also began to greatly urbanize. Factories mainly occurred in cities, allowing larger proportions of people to live and work in the city, rather than in the country. **Millionaire cities**, each with at least one million people, began to emerge and spread. By 1800, London became the first millionaire city.

A series of political revolutions emerged, starting with the French Revolution in the late 1700s. The phenomenon of nationalism began in Europe. **Nationalism** refers to a process where a nation seeks political representation. A new form of territoriality, the nation-state, began to appear. Democracy began to be a more common phenomenon in Europe at this time, though its roots are in Greece about 2,000 years ago.[11]

Primate City

A **primate city** refers to one that is the economic core of a country and has a population more than twice as large as any other city. London, Paris, and Athens are examples of primate cities in Europe.[12] Over half of the capital cities of the countries in Europe are considered primate cities.

Notre Dame Cathedral

Notre Dame de Paris is the medieval Roman Catholic cathedral that resides on Cite Island in the middle of the Seine River of Paris, France. Construction started in 1163 and finished in 1345, although many changes have occurred across the centuries. Most recently, a fire in April 2019 destroyed the spire and the majority of the roof of this iconic French Gothic architectural wonder.

PARIS, FRANCE – Cathedral Notre Dame de Paris.

© Kiev.Victor/Shutterstock.com

Language Patterns

Within the Europe region there is a broad unity of language. The Indo-European language family predominates over most of the region. However, within this broad unity there is much regional diversity. *The Germanic language group* dominates in northern and western Europe. Norwegian, Swedish, Danish, German, Dutch, Flemish, and English are examples of Germanic languages.

The *Romance language group* is used in southern Europe. Portuguese, Spanish, French, and Italian are examples of Romance languages. In eastern Europe, the Romanian language is also a Romance language. The Slavic language group of eastern Europe includes Polish, Czech, Slovakian, Slovenian, Croatian, Serbian, and Ukrainian.

The *Celtic language group* is found in the remote western edges of the Europe region. Scottish and Irish Gaelic, Welsh, and Breton are examples of Celtic languages. The only non-Indo-European languages in Europe are Finnish, Estonian, Hungarian (Uralic language family), the Basque language in Spain,[13] and the Maltese (Semitic language) in Malta.

Religion Patterns

Similar to language, a broad religious unity exists in Europe but with regional diversity. Christianity is represented over most of Europe however, it is on the decline in many countries. it is broken into *three main sects of Christianity*. **Protestant Christianity** is practiced in northern and western Europe, with Lutheran Protestantism in Scandinavia and northern Germany and Anglican Protestantism in the United Kingdom.

Roman Catholic Christianity is found in southern Europe and the northern and western Slavic areas. Portugal, Spain, France, Italy, Poland, Czech Republic, Slovenia, and Croatia are examples. **Orthodox Christianity** predominates in the southern and interior parts of eastern Europe. Serbia, Greece, Bulgaria, Ukraine, and Russia are examples.

Islam predominates in Albania and Kosovo but is a growing religion in Europe.[14] Demographers believe that this religion will grow by 2050 due to the migrants, asylum seekers, and refugees who have sought out the region.

Population

About[15] 743 million people live in the Europe region. Most of the population is found within the North European Lowland (Plain). Given its high level of economic development, Europe is experiencing slow growth or negative growth. Most countries fall below replacement rate fertility levels. Thus, much of Europe is in the population implosion stage (stage 5) of the demographic transition model, with very low birth rates and low but rising death rates. For many European countries deaths, are annually higher than births.

Political Forces

At any one time, a place is affected by two sets of opposite forces: centripetal forces and centrifugal forces. **Centripetal forces are any factors that** lead to unity, integration, and bonding. Common language, common religion, and common ethnicity are examples of such forces. **Centrifugal forces** are any factors that lead to disunity or division. Different languages, different religions, and different ethnic groups are examples of centrifugal forces.

Devolution

An important type of centrifugal force is devolution. **Devolution** is a process whereby a large area is divided into smaller areas or whereby a central government provides certain areas with some degree of local autonomy, such as local parliaments. The division of former Czechoslovakia into the Czech Republic and Slovakia and the division of former Yugoslavia into Slovenia, Croatia, Serbia, Bosnia, Macedonia, Montenegro, and Kosovo are examples of dividing large areas into smaller areas. An example of the other type of devolution would be the United Kingdom allowing Scotland, Wales, and Northern Ireland to have their own local parliaments. Another example is Spain, which has allowed the Basque country in the north central part of Spain, Galicia in the northwest, and Catalonia in the northeast to have local parliaments or some local control.[18]

The Emerging European Union

An important type of centripetal force is supranationalism. **Supranationalism** is a venture that involves three or more states joining together for some mutual benefit.

Flags of the European Union. EU flag in the middle.

© Belish/Shutterstock.com

The first major example of supranationalism in Europe occurred near the end of World War II. In 1944, three small states in Western Europe, the Benelux countries, formed the Benelux Union. The **Benelux** countries are Belgium, Netherlands, and Luxembourg. The Benelux Union was a customs union where the three countries decided to economically unite for economic purposes but remained politically independent.

In 1951 the three Benelux countries joined France, Italy, and West Germany to form a limited economic organization. This limited organization worked well enough that the same six states met in Rome in 1957 and signed the Treaty of Rome. The result was the **European Economic Community (EEC)**, also known as the Common Market. By the mid-1960s, the EEC created a council, a court,

One euro coin.

© AnnaGarmatiy/Shutterstock.com

a parliament, a commission, and changed its name to the **European Community (EC)**.

In 1991, the EC became the **European Union (EU)**. The EU has a common currency, the euro[19](€), which most countries in the EU have adopted. Countries in the EU also share common foreign policies, a common passport system with free movement between member states, extensive economic integration, and tough environmental laws. Over time, the European Union has expanded to a twenty-eight-member organization. In the early 1970s,

LONDON, UK: Brexit suporters (brexiteers) in central London holding banners campaigning to leave the European Union. (January 2019)

© Ink Drop/Shutterstock.com

Denmark, the United Kingdom, and the Republic of Ireland joined. In the 1980s, Spain, Portugal, and Greece were admitted, making it a twelve-member group. In the mid-1990s, Austria, Sweden, and Finland joined. In 2004, ten countries joined all at once. These ten new countries were Estonia, Latvia, Lithuania, Poland, the Czech Republic, Slovakia, Hungary, Slovenia, Malta, and the Greek-controlled part of Cyprus. In 2007, Romania and Bulgaria were added. In 2013, Croatia became the twenty-eighth member state. It is often easier to remember what parts of Europe are not in the EU. Iceland, Norway, Switzerland, Serbia, and several other states in southeast Europe are not yet members.[17] Soon the twenty-eight-country EU will experience the **Brexit** (British + Exit) of the United Kingdom, as it officially leaves the EU. Although the deadline has moved, it appears that by summer of 2019 the United Kingdom will once again be solely in control of their own economy.

Subregions of Europe[19]

There are five different subregions of the Europe region. These smaller areas include Western Europe, the British Isles, Mediterranean Europe, Northern Europe, and Eastern Europe.[20]

Western Europe

Western Europe includes the countries of Germany, France,[21] Austria, Liechtenstein, Switzerland, and the Benelux countries. This subregion is the economic and demographic core of the Europe region. It is primarily Protestant Christian and Germanic-speaking.

Germany is the most populated and economically developed country in Europe. Within west central Germany is the Ruhr, an economic and demographic core of Germany. It includes a series of large cities closely connected together with steel, metal manufacturing, and chemical processing.

France holds the largest land area in Western Europe and is its most important agricultural and food producing country. Paris is an excellent example of a primate city. Unlike most of Western Europe, France is dominantly Romance-speaking and Catholic Christian.[22]

Austria, Liechtenstein, and Switzerland are countries known for their Alpine beauty, with Europe's highest mountain range (the Alps) making up their dominant topography. Switzerland is often recognized as a neutral country and is not part of the EU today, like the microstate of Liechtenstein. Austria is a country known for its baroque and classical music, and its primate city and capital Vienna proudly showcases that legacy.

The Netherlands is a small, densely populated country west of Germany. Within the Netherlands there is an important area known as the Randstad, it is comprised of the *three largest Dutch cities*: *Amsterdam*, *Rotterdam*, and *The Hague*. The Randstad is the economic and population core of the Netherlands. **Rotterdam**, at the mouth of the Rhine River, is Europe's largest port and one of the largest ports in the world.[23] The Netherlands is often referred to as Holland, due to the provinces in the country that once dominated the area.

Windmill reflected in the Kinderdijk canal in South Holland, Netherlands.

© EyesTravelling/Shutterstock.com

Belgium is located west of Germany and north of France. Belgium is an excellent example of a binational state. Most people in the north are Flemish-speaking and Protestant Christian. Most people in the south are Walloons, French-speaking, and Catholic Christian. Brussels is the capital city of Belgium and a major headquarters city of the European Union. A minority in the country speak German.[24] Belgium is also known for its complicated government that has multiple levels of governing power.

The last of the Benelux countries is Luxembourg, which is the last grand duchy in Europe. It is a small country with a strong economy and is typically listed as one of the richest countries in the world.

British Isles

The **British Isles** includes two major islands, Britain and Ireland [25] and thousands of other small islands. Two countries comprise this subregion: the United Kingdom of Great Britain and Northern Ireland and the Republic of Ireland.[26]

The **United Kingdom** (**UK**) includes the[27] constituent countries of England, Scotland, Wales, and Northern Ireland. London, the capital of the UK[28] and England, is an excellent example of a primate city. During the term of former Prime Minister Tony Blair, Scotland, Wales, and Northern Ireland were allowed to form their own local parliaments. There is still much intense nationalism within Scotland, which voted in 2014 to stay within the UK rather than become independent. The UK is largely Anglican Protestant Christian and Germanic-speaking.[29] It is separated from mainland Europe by the English Channel, which is less than 21 miles wide at its narrowest point.

London aerial view with Tower Bridge on the River Thames.
© ESB Professional/Shutterstock.com

The Republic of Ireland consists of the southern three-fourths of the island of Ireland, and it became independent in the early twentieth century. It is predominantly Catholic Christian and Germanic-speaking, but the Irish Gaelic language is also important in literature and history. During the 1980s and 1990s, the Republic of Ireland experienced remarkable economic growth, quickly shifting from a less developed economy to a more-developed economy. This quick transformation earned it the nickname **Celtic Tiger** (a quickly transforming[30] economy that pounces like a tiger into the global market). High-tech manufacturing and research, along with finance and tourism, fueled the economic transition in Ireland.[31]

Mediterranean Europe

Mediterranean Europe includes the countries of Italy, Spain,[32] Portugal, Greece; the microstates of Monaco, Andorra, Malta, San Marino, Vatican City; and part of the island of Cyprus. Romance languages and Catholic Christianity are used over most of the subregion. This part of Europe is characterized by a humid temperate (mild) Mediterranean climate. Topographically, it is a hilly and mountainous area.[33]

Looking down over Piazza San Pietro in Vatican City
© Banauke/Shutterstock.com

Italy is the most populated country within Mediterranean Europe. It is also the most economically-developed country in the subregion and the country most connected to the European core. Within Italy, the **Ancona Line** separates the more developed north from the less developed south. It extends from the city of Ancona on the east coast to just south of Rome on the west coast. In the more developed north, the main economic and population core is the Po River Valley, including the city of Milan. Milan is Italy's main industrial and financial center.

Spain is the larger country of the *Iberian Peninsula*. It is an excellent example of devolution. The central government in Madrid allows Catalonia, the Basque country, and Galicia to have local parliaments. Catalonia, the province in the northeast that includes Barcelona, is especially active in seeking possible independence.[34] Spain is the only country in Europe that directly touches the lands of Africa by way of their enclaves that share a border with Morocco.

Portugal, also on the Iberian Peninsula, sits on the far western edge of Europe. It was once a large empire and had lands across the world. Portugal is known for its diverse agricultural exports, including being the largest producer of cork in the world.

Greece is the major country on the Balkan Peninsula. The Greek language is Indo-European but not part of the Romance language group. Greeks practice the Greek Orthodox Christian religion, rather than Catholic Christian. Greece experienced [35] severe economic problems, requiring massive financial aid from the rest of the European Union.[36] The financial debt payments to the EU will take until 2060 to pay off entirely.

Six **microstates** (very small sovereign states) are situated in Europe, five of which are in this subregion: Monaco, Andorra, Malta, San Marino, and Vatican City. Monaco is just over three-fourths of a square mile and is part of the French Riviera. It is known for the city of Monte Carlo and its historic casino. Andorra is ruled by two co-princes, sits high in the Pyrenees mountains, and attracts tourists for duty-free shopping and ski resorts. Malta is an archipelago south of Italy in the Mediterranean Sea. It was historically a shipping stop but is today popular with tourists for its Mediterranean climate and sunshine. San Marino is an *enclave* in Italy with a view of the Adriatic Sea but landlocked along the edge of the Apennine Mountains. Vatican City is the smallest country in the world with a .17-square mile area. It is the home of Roman Catholicism and the Pope. It is known for its spectacular architecture and artwork, including the Sistine Chapel.

The island of Cyprus is located in the eastern Mediterranean Sea. It is a good example of a binational territory, with Turkish Cypriots controlling the north and Greek Cypriots controlling the south. In 2004, the Greek part of Cyprus was admitted into the European Union,[37] and only part of the island is considered in the region of Europe politically.

Note: The **Rock of Gibraltar** and the lands of Gibraltar are also location in this subregion, even though they are politically tied to the United Kingdom as an overseas territory. The Spanish

The Monaco Port

© tichr/Shutterstock.com

have made claims to the land, but as the land lies next to the **Strait of Gibraltar** and is one of the only two Mediterranean Sea entry/exit ways, it is considered a geostrategic choke point that the British will not relinquish.

Northern Europe

Northern Europe includes the countries of Norway, Sweden, Denmark, Finland and[38] Iceland. It is an area commonly referred to as Scandinavia,[39] as both Norway and Sweden sit on the Scandinavian Peninsula. Germanic languages and Lutheran Protestant Christianity are common here. Northern Europe has high standards of living and quality of life indicators[40] but smaller populations in which to contend. Sweden has the largest population of ten million people and is often seen as the leader of the subregion. Politically,[41] Northern Europe is dominated by democratic socialism, with the central governments' providing "cradle-to-grave" health insurance and a strong government presence in people's lives. The subregion is impacted greatly by glaciers, emphasizes very progressive attitudes, with relatively high proportions of females in government and economic activities. Though influenced by Lutheranism, most of the countries are highly secular (religion being a small part of most people's lives).[42]

Denmark, sitting on the *Jutland Peninsula*, is the major player in agriculture for the subregion, as many of the other countries have shorter growing seasons. Its geostrategic position, where the North Sea and the Baltic Sea meet, gives it an economic trade advantage. Finland is positively economically impacted by the **taiga**, the coniferous forests that run the length of the northern portion of **Eurasia** (the name given to European and Asian continents when combined). Iceland, isolated by distance in the North Atlantic Ocean, has largely Scandinavian culture and sits on volcanic ridge of the **Mid-Atlantic Ridge**, which is the longest mountain range in the world, although underwater.

The picturesque sunset over landscapes and waterfalls at Kirkjufell Mountain in Iceland.

© Standret/Shutterstock.com

Eastern Europe

Eastern Europe includes the countries of Poland, Estonia, Latvia, Lithuania, the Czech Republic, Slovakia, Hungary, Romania, Bulgaria, Slovenia, Croatia, Bosnia and Herzegovina, Serbia, Montenegro,[43] Moldova, North Macedonia, Kosovo, Albania, and the Ukraine. It is dominated by Slavic languages and Christianity. The northern and western Slavs are largely Catholic Christian, whereas the southern and eastern Slavs are Orthodox Christian. This subregion was formerly under the control of the former Soviet Union is communist economy and government. Since the early 1990s, it has been transitioning from a communist command economy and communist government to a[44] free market economy and democracy.[45] Many of the Eastern European countries are considered the poorest in Europe.

Town Hall Square (Latvian Ratslaukums) is one of the central squares of Riga, located in the Old Town, Latvia.

© V_E/Shutterstock.com

Poland, as well as the Baltic states of *Estonia*, *Latvia*, and *Lithuania*, makes up a nearly continuous arc around the southern and eastern edge of the Baltic Sea. Russia's exclave, **Kaliningrad**, sits between the countries of Poland and Lithuania and gives Russia a port in the Baltic, which is ice-free year-round. Many of the Eastern European countries are landlocked, but, due to their proximity to the Danube River, the countries of Slovakia, Hungary, Serbia, and Moldova now have access to the Black Sea and the Mediterranean sea via the Bosporus Strait. Countries such as Romania, Bulgaria, and the Ukraine have immediate access to the Black Sea, giving them valuable real estate.

The devolution of former Czechoslovakia into the Czech Republic and Slovakia occurred so smoothly that it is often referred to as the **Velvet Divorce**.[46] Conversely, other parts of Eastern Europe[47] make an excellent example of a **shatter belt**, an area that has been externally and internally splintered and fractured. The external shattering occurs largely as a result of the relative location of Eastern Europe. Historically, Germans from the west, Russians/Soviets from the east, and Ottoman Turks from the south created chronic fracturing and splintering in this subregion. Internally, shattering is a result of a tremendous diversity of

Budapest, Hungary on the Danube River.

© TTstudio/Shutterstock.com

different ethnic groups, religions, and languages.[48] Many of the countries also sit on the Balkan Peninsula, so the term **balkanization** is often used to describe the ethnic splintering.

Ethnocentrism is the common tendency of an ethnic group to consider that group to be more important than other groups. **Ethnic cleansing** is an extreme form of ethnocentrism, in which an ethnic group seeks to remove or obliterate another group to ensure its superior-

Gjeravica, the highest mountain of Kosovo

© HrMiro/Shutterstock.com

ity. Another name for ethnic cleansing is **genocide**. In Eastern Europe, two examples of ethnic cleansing are the states of Bosnia and Kosovo.

In Bosnia and Herzegovina, there are three main ethnic groups: *Bosnian Croats, Bosnian Serbs*, and *Bosnian Muslims (Bosniaks)*. Until the early 1990s, these three groups managed to coexist without major problems. With the dissolution of former Yugoslavia in the early 1990s, former republics, such as Bosnia, sought political independence. The Bosnian Serbs, aided by Serbian officials and military, sought to assemble all the Serbs together to form a Greater Serbia. The Serbs began to ethnically cleanse the area of Croats and especially Muslims; **NATO** (The North Atlantic Treaty Organization) and UN troops were dispatched to the area to end the genocide.

In Kosovo, the majority of the population were ethnic Kosovars (Albanian-speaking Muslims). Kosovo used to be a political part of Serbia, symbolically representing the core area of early Serb culture. To provide long-term Serbian control of this culturally important area, the Serbs began to cleanse the area of Kosovars. Again, NATO and UN troops were dispatched to end the ethnic cleansing. Eventually, the Kosovars unilaterally seceded from Serbia and formed a politically independent Kosovo,[49] although not all countries in the world recognize Kosovo's independence.

Ukraine has the largest land area within the Europe region. It is strategically

All-green spring in the Tunnel of Love, Ukraine

© Vitalia_Ponomarova/Shutterstock.com

located between Russia to the east and more democratic states to the west. Internally, western Ukraine is rural, agricultural, Catholic Christian, and ethnically Ukrainian. Eastern Ukraine is more urban, industrial, and Orthodox Christian with sizable concentrations of ethnic Russians. Russia annexed the Crimea peninsula[50] in 2014 and supported ethnic Russian efforts in eastern Ukraine to achieve independence from the Ukraine government. This[51] policy, called **irredentism** (political favoritism to restore relations or territory to a former country), contributes to the country's political instability.[52]

Review Terms[53]

Alpine System
Ancona Line
Balkanization
Benelux
Brexit
British Isles
Celtic Tiger
centrifugal forces
centripetal forces
devolution
Eastern Europe
ethnic cleansing
ethnocentrism
Eurasia
European
    Community (EC)

EEC
European Union (EU)
genocide
industrial revolution
irredentism
Kaliningrad
Mediterranean Europe
microstates
Mid-Atlantic Ridge
millionaire cities
nationalism
NATO
North Atlantic Current
North European Lowland
Northern Europe
Orthodox Christianity

peninsula
primate city
Protestant Christianity
Rock of Gibraltar
Roman Catholic Christianity
Rotterdam
shatter belt
Strait of Gibraltar
supranationalism
taiga
United Kingdom (UK)
Velvet Divorce
Western Europe

Research Topics

city-state
conurbation
Eurozone
exclave
fjord
four motors of Europe
local functional specialization
Schengen Agreement
site
situation
Warsaw Pact
World Trade Organization
world-city

Credits

26. **Source:** From Thomas J. Karwoski, *World Regional Geography: An Introduction*, 1st ed., Copyright © 2016 by Kendall Hunt Publishing Company. Reprinted by permission.
27. **Source:** From Thomas J. Karwoski, *World Regional Geography: An Introduction*, 1st ed., Copyright © 2016 by Kendall Hunt Publishing Company. Reprinted by permission.
28. **Source:** From Thomas J. Karwoski, *World Regional Geography: An Introduction*, 1st ed., Copyright © 2016 by Kendall Hunt Publishing Company. Reprinted by permission.
29. **Source:** From Thomas J. Karwoski, *World Regional Geography: An Introduction*, 1st ed., Copyright © 2016 by Kendall Hunt Publishing Company. Reprinted by permission.
30. **Source:** From Thomas J. Karwoski, *World Regional Geography: An Introduction*, 1st ed., Copyright © 2016 by Kendall Hunt Publishing Company. Reprinted by permission.
31. **Source:** From Thomas J. Karwoski, *World Regional Geography: An Introduction*, 1st ed., Copyright © 2016 by Kendall Hunt Publishing Company. Reprinted by permission.
32. **Source:** From Thomas J. Karwoski, *World Regional Geography: An Introduction*, 1st ed., Copyright © 2016 by Kendall Hunt Publishing Company. Reprinted by permission.
33. **Source:** From Thomas J. Karwoski, *World Regional Geography: An Introduction*, 1st ed., Copyright © 2016 by Kendall Hunt Publishing Company. Reprinted by permission.
34. **Source:** From Thomas J. Karwoski, *World Regional Geography: An Introduction*, 1st ed., Copyright © 2016 by Kendall Hunt Publishing Company. Reprinted by permission.
35. **Source:** From Thomas J. Karwoski, *World Regional Geography: An Introduction*, 1st ed., Copyright © 2016 by Kendall Hunt Publishing Company. Reprinted by permission.
36. **Source:** From Thomas J. Karwoski, *World Regional Geography: An Introduction*, 1st ed., Copyright © 2016 by Kendall Hunt Publishing Company. Reprinted by permission.
37. **Source:** From Thomas J. Karwoski, *World Regional Geography: An Introduction*, 1st ed., Copyright © 2016 by Kendall Hunt Publishing Company. Reprinted by permission.
38. **Source:** From Thomas J. Karwoski, *World Regional Geography: An Introduction*, 1st ed., Copyright © 2016 by Kendall Hunt Publishing Company. Reprinted by permission.
39. **Source:** From Thomas J. Karwoski, *World Regional Geography: An Introduction*, 1st ed., Copyright © 2016 by Kendall Hunt Publishing Company. Reprinted by permission.
40. **Source:** From Thomas J. Karwoski, *World Regional Geography: An Introduction*, 1st ed., Copyright © 2016 by Kendall Hunt Publishing Company. Reprinted by permission.
41. **Source:** From Thomas J. Karwoski, *World Regional Geography: An Introduction*, 1st ed., Copyright © 2016 by Kendall Hunt Publishing Company. Reprinted by permission.
42. **Source:** From Thomas J. Karwoski, *World Regional Geography: An Introduction*, 1st ed., Copyright © 2016 by Kendall Hunt Publishing Company. Reprinted by permission.
43. **Source:** From Thomas J. Karwoski, *World Regional Geography: An Introduction*, 1st ed., Copyright © 2016 by Kendall Hunt Publishing Company. Reprinted by permission.
44. **Source:** From Thomas J. Karwoski, *World Regional Geography: An Introduction*, 1st ed., Copyright © 2016 by Kendall Hunt Publishing Company. Reprinted by permission.
45. **Source:** From Thomas J. Karwoski, *World Regional Geography: An Introduction*, 1st ed., Copyright © 2016 by Kendall Hunt Publishing Company. Reprinted by permission.
46. **Source:** From Thomas J. Karwoski, *World Regional Geography: An Introduction*, 1st ed., Copyright © 2016 by Kendall Hunt Publishing Company. Reprinted by permission.
47. **Source:** From Thomas J. Karwoski, *World Regional Geography: An Introduction*, 1st ed., Copyright © 2016 by Kendall Hunt Publishing Company. Reprinted by permission.
48. **Source:** From Thomas J. Karwoski, *World Regional Geography: An Introduction*, 1st ed., Copyright © 2016 by Kendall Hunt Publishing Company. Reprinted by permission.
49. **Source:** From Thomas J. Karwoski, *World Regional Geography: An Introduction*, 1st ed., Copyright © 2016 by Kendall Hunt Publishing Company. Reprinted by permission.
50. **Source:** From Thomas J. Karwoski, *World Regional Geography: An Introduction*, 1st ed., Copyright © 2016 by Kendall Hunt Publishing Company. Reprinted by permission.
51. **Source:** From Thomas J. Karwoski, *World Regional Geography: An Introduction*, 1st ed., Copyright © 2016 by Kendall Hunt Publishing Company. Reprinted by permission.
52. **Source:** From Thomas J. Karwoski, *World Regional Geography: An Introduction*, 1st ed., Copyright © 2016 by Kendall Hunt Publishing Company. Reprinted by permission.
53. **Source:** From Thomas J. Karwoski, *World Regional Geography: An Introduction*, 1st ed., Copyright © 2016 by Kendall Hunt Publishing Company. Reprinted by permission.

Chapter 6

RUSSIA, TRANSCAUCASIA, AND CENTRAL ASIA

It is a riddle wrapped in a mystery inside an enigma.

—Winston Churchill on Russia

Where Are Russia, Transcaucasia, and Central Asia?

As a region, Russia includes the country of Russia,[1] Transcaucasia,[2] and the Central Asian (Turkestan) countries. This region resides in the Northern Hemisphere and nearly completely in the Eastern Hemisphere. The Transcaucus and Central Asian countries sit on the Eurasian tectonic plate, as does most of Russia, although the far eastern edge resides on the North American tectonic plate.

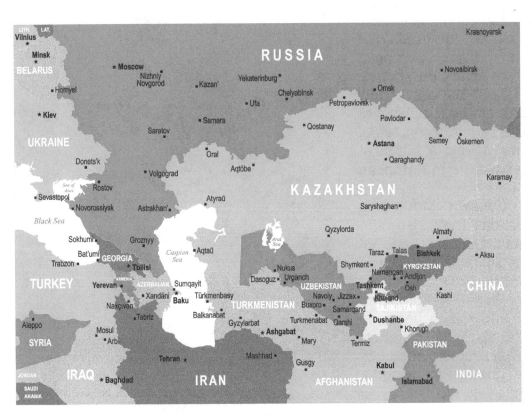

The Russian, Transcaucasian, and Central Asian Region

© dikobraziy/Shutterstock.com

Major Qualities of Russia

Russia is the largest state in size of land area in the world, overlapping the continents of Europe and Asia. The northernmost populous country in the world, it has comparatively few people (approximately[3] 143.9 million) for such an immense physical footprint. An advantage of its massive land area is a rich variety of resources, including much oil and natural gas. Russia is, in reality, a multiethnic, multicultural state with the Russian ethnic group being the largest in numbers and proportion. Since the early 1900s, Russia has experienced rapid political, economic, and social change, with most of the change happening since the 1990s.[4]

Landform Patterns

The **Ural Mountains** form a north-south trending mountain system in west central Russia that is commonly used as a boundary between the continent of Europe to the west and the continent of Asia to the east. Within Russia, the mountains divide European Russia from Asiatic Russia. The Asiatic part of Russia is broadly referred to as **Siberia**. Most of the land area and resources of Russia are in Siberia, but most of the people are in European Russia.

The **Caucasus Mountains** are a west-east trending mountain system that lies between the Black Sea and the Caspian Sea. Like the Urals, they are a boundary between Europe to the north and Asia to the south. They also mark the historical and cultural southern boundary of Russia. Russia is in the north; non-Russia is in the south.[5]

Most of European Russia is comprised of the Russian Plain, the eastern extension of the North European Plain. Most of Russia's people, agriculture,

The Caspian Sea is the world's largest inland body of water.

© Rainer Lesniewski/Shutterstock.com

and industry are on the Russian Plain. Russia is a **transcontinental** (sitting on more than one continent) country.[6] The Black Sea and the Caspian Sea also historic boundaries between the continents of Europe and Asia. The Caspian Sea is the largest lake in the world, based on surface area and average volume of water.[7] The Aral Sea was the fourth largest lake in the world, but today it is made up of several small lakes and is an environmental disaster in Central Asia, due to extreme water diversion projects.

Lake Baikal, in South Central Siberia,[8] is the world's deepest lake, the world's oldest lake, and one of the clearest lakes in the world. The Volga River is the major river of movement of goods and people in Russia. It flows north to south across the Russian Plain, emptying into the Caspian Sea.

Climate Patterns

Given the latitude and position of the high middle latitudes, the dominant climate type is a humid cold climate, also known as a continental location climate. Summers are short and cool, and winters are long and cold. Precipitation levels are low. The large continental landmass is a major factor in creating these climate conditions.

Lake Baikal. Irkutsk region, Russia.
© Nikitin Victor/Shutterstock.com

Forward Capital

A **forward capital** is a capital city located or relocated away from the historic core toward the periphery, indicating the intent of a state to develop the newer area. In Russia, St. Petersburg is a classic example of a forward capital.

Czar Peter the Great decided to locate the capital of the Russian Empire at St. Petersburg, named in his honor, so that it would be Russia's "window to the west." He intended to reorient

Winter Palace in Saint Petersburg, Russia.
© V_E/Shutterstock.com

Russia toward Europe and the western side of Eurasia and brought in architects and designers to create a more European-like city.[9]

Recent Political and Economic Changes

Until the early 1900s, the Russian Empire was a feudal, medieval state. Czars (tsars) ruled a country of mostly poor, landless people. In 1917, in St. Petersburg, the Russian Empire collapsed with the overthrow and assassination of Czar Nicholas II and his family. Vladimir Lenin led a group of **Bolsheviks** (a faction of Russian Communists), representing a broad coalition of business people, workers, and peasants.

Lenin who replaced the tsars, created the **Union of Soviet Socialist Republics (USSR)**, and introduced communism as a political and economic system. A hallmark feature of communism as an economic system was the com-

Russian Royal family in 1914. L-R Seated: Marie, Queen Alexandra, Czar Nicholas II, Anastasia, Alexei. Standing: Olga and Tatiana.

© Everett Historical/Shutterstock.com

mand economy. The **command economy** was based on centralized economic planning with bureaucrats in Moscow (the new capital) making all economic decisions. Under the command economy, everyone has a job, and the government subsidizes housing and food. Although an equitable system, it was highly inefficient.

Moscow, Russia- Lenin's Mausoleum in Red Square is the resting place of Vladimir Lenin.

© Tomasz Wozniak/Shutterstock.com

By the 1970s and 1980s, economic and social problems increased in scope and numbers. Many people became frustrated with the lack of food, the quality of goods, and the lack of basic liberties like freedom to travel and freedom of speech. In the late 1980s, Mikhail Gorbachev was the Soviet leader. He recognized the numerous problems and believed some action was needed to prevent the collapse of communism. Gorbachev proposed two major strategies to try to save the Soviet Union: glasnost and perestroika.

Glasnost referred to Gorbachev's intent to open up and liberalize Soviet society. Soviet citizens would have more freedom to travel within and outside the country. More freedom of speech would be encouraged. Greater access to Western goods and clothing would become available. **Perestroika** referred to Gorbachev's intent to restructure the Soviet economy away from a command economy toward a more market-based Western economy.

Before Gorbachev could implement these changes, he was replaced by Boris Yeltsin, a popular mayor of Moscow. It was actually Yeltsin who began to implement these changes. In the early 1990s, the Soviet Union collapsed, and communism as an economic and political system began to fall. Price controls were removed. State-owned businesses were sold to private investors. People could own property and sell goods on their own.

However, many problems and issues remain. Food and housing are now much more expensive. Inefficient factories and businesses have shut down, greatly increasing unemployment. The Russian "Mafia" has rapidly increased its presence and influence.[10]

Population

Of the[11] 233 million people in the region, 143 million people live in the country of Russia, about[13] 17 million people live in Transcaucasia,[14] and 73 million people live in Central Asia. The country of Russia is experiencing population implosion, due to low birth rates and rising death rates (especially among middle-aged males). Population in Russia will likely continue to fall over the next few decades,[15] even with the National Day of Conceptions being instituted.

Vladimir Ilyich Ulyanov Lenin, 1920. Lenin encouraged colonial nations to socialist revolution against imperialists.

© Everett Historical/Shutterstock.com

"Order of Maternal Glory" created by Stalin to award mothers with high numbers of children.

© Chiffanna/Shutterstock.com

Russian women are having fewer babies and at a below replacement fertility rate. Death rates have risen, due to exposure to unchecked environmental pollution, increased cancer and suicide rates among middle-age males, and a rapid increase in murders. Most of the population resides in the European part of Russia, with the attraction of the Russian Plain is more favorable climate and soil conditions.[16]

Geopolitics

Geopolitics is the study of how place or location affects political behavior. There are two geopolitical theories to consider, the heartland theory and the rimland theory.

In the early 1900s, British geographer Halford Mackinder introduced the most well-known theory of geopolitics: the **heartland theory**. According to Mackinder, whoever rules Eastern Europe and European Russia controls the "heartland." Who rules the heartland controls Eurasia. Who rules Eurasia controls the world. The path to global domination thus starts in Eastern Europe and European Russia. In the early twentieth century, naval warfare dominated military strategy. A land-based location like Eastern Europe and European Russia would be relatively immune to naval attack but could consolidate power and expand outward. After the end of the Second World War, the Soviet Union was in control of all of Russia, Eastern Europe, and much of central Asia.

In the mid-1900s, an American researcher, Nicholas Spykman, introduced an alternate theory of geopolitics: the **rimland theory**. According to Spykman, who rules the fringe of Europe, Africa, and Asia controls the rimland. Who rules the rimland controls Eurasia. Who rules Eurasia controls the destiny of the world.[17]

The Russian, Transcaucasian, and Central Asian Region[18]

There are three subregions in this region: Russia, Transcaucasia, and Central Asia.

Russia

The **Russian Core** spatially coincides with the Russian Plain, the European part of Russia. Most of the population, industry, and agriculture are located here. Within the Russian Core the focus is the Central Industrial District. The Central Industrial District is based on the city of Moscow, the political, economic, and population center of Russia. The centrality of Moscow ensures that, all decisions originate and diffuse from there.

Panoramic view of the old Red Square with Kremlin and St Basil's Cathedral in Moscow, Russia.

© Viacheslav Lopatin/Shutterstock.com

The North Caucasus is part of the Russian Core on the north side of the Caucasus Mountains. It is politically still part of the country of Russia. In the mind of ethnic Russians, the true border of Russia is culturally and politically the Caucasus Mountains. The North Caucasus includes a number of territories, such as Chechnya and Dagestan. This area of Russia includes mostly non-Russian ethnic groups who tend to be dominantly Muslim, such as the Dagestanis and the Chechens. The north Caucasus is an area of intense political and ethnic instability within Russia. Intense nationalism and the dominance of Islam provide the basis for much of the conflict in this area, especially in Chechnya.[19]

Chechnya mosque in Russia.

© prdyapim/Shutterstock.com

Transcaucasia

Transcaucasia refers to the part of this region south of the Caucasus Mountains. Transcaucasia used to be part of the Soviet Union. It now includes three politically independent states: Georgia, Armenia, and Azerbaijan. Russia recently invaded two areas in Georgia with the intent of assisting ethnic Russians. These two areas are Abkhazia, in northwest Georgia, and South Ossetia, in north central Georgia.

Yerevan, capital of Armenia at the sunrise with the two peaks of the Mount Ararat on the background.

© MehmetO/Shutterstock.com

Armenia has been in conflict with Azerbaijan over an area known as Nagorno-Karabakh, a territory within the political borders of Azerbaijan, but comprised of mainly Armenians. Armenia has been trying to unite the Armenians in Nagorno-Karabakh with the rest of Christian Armenia. Muslim-dominated Azerbaijan resists the loss of any of its territory. Religion and ethnicity provide the basis for much instability between these two countries. Azerbaijan, with newly discovered oil deposits off its Caspian Sea coast, is an emerging major oil producer within the subregion.[20]

Central Asia

Central Asia includes the historic area known as **Turkestan**, which refers to the five former Soviet-controlled republics that are now politically independent. These five states are largely Islamic in religion, and most people speak a Turkish-related language. Both cultural elements are remnants of the Ottoman Empire. Each of the Turkestan states is dominated by different ethnic and language groups.[21]

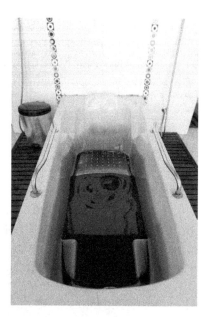

Naftalan, Azerbaijan. Oil treatment bath

© alionabirukova/Shutterstock.com

Central Asia has a mostly arid climate, though rivers from its high mountain areas allow for irrigated agriculture. Ethnic tensions have also been significant in Central Asia, often in the form of anti-Russian sentiments after many years of Soviet efforts to **Russify** (make it Russian) the region or as a result of non-participatory, and autocratic regimes. Its population is the fastest growing among the territories that were once part of the Soviet Union.[22]

Kazakhstan is the largest of the Turkestan states in land area. The Kazakh ethnic group is the major ethnicity. It is economically dominated by cotton, uranium, and oil production.[23] The country also has substantial environmental problems from Soviet nuclear testing, industrial dereliction, and ecological problems of the Area Sea.[24]

Uzbekistan is the most populated Turkestan state[25] and is **double landlocked**, which means it is a landlocked country surrounded by other landlocked countries.[26] It is centrally located within the area and adjoins all the other states. The Uzkbeks are the dominant ethnic group.[27]

Turkmenistan, dominated by the Turkmen,[28] has access to rich natural gas and oil reserves on the Caspian Sea. It has been ruled by authoritarian regimes that discriminate against minority groups and severely limit the rights of their populations in general,[29] as is the case for Uzbekistan.[30]

Kyrgyzstan, dominated by the Kyrgyz,[31] the Tian Shan mountain range, bordering China and the Issyk-Kul Lake, the second largest mountain lake in the world. Some researchers believe that the black plague originated in the lake in the 14th century, killing 75 million people across China, South Asia, Europe, and North Africa.[32]

Baiterek Tower the symbol of modern Astana, capital of Kazakhstan.

© Piu_Piu/Shutterstock.com

The Aral Sea

The Aral Sea is fed by two rivers that drain from the Pamir Range. The Syr Darya flows through Kazakhstan and enters the lake from the north. The more important river is the Amu Darya, which flows through Uzbekistan and Turkmenistan and enters the lake from the south. In ancient times, the Amu Darya has sometimes changed course and drained into the Caspian Sea instead, leaving the Aral Sea largely dry. In modern times, however, the diversion of river waters for agriculture (especially water-intensive cotton) in Kazakhstan, Uzbekistan, and Turkmenistan, along with a severe drought in the mid-2000s, almost drained the entire lake. This is sometimes regarded as the greatest human-induced disaster in the world, as the shrinking lake poisoned the land and people with salt, heavy metals and pesticide. Today the Aral Sea is only about one-tenth the size it was before 1960, when it was the fourth largest lake in the world. Animals and people who were once dependent on the Aral Sea have either migrated to other areas or died. The North Aral Sea is the only area to have had substantial ecological restoration work conducted on it, which has been reasonably successful. Further efforts are underway.

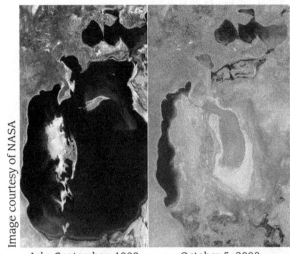

Image courtesy of NASA

July–September, 1989   October 5, 2008

Image source: NASA Earth Observatory (US Government public domain), see also http://en.wikipedia.0rg/wiki/File:Aral_Sea_1989-2008.jpg
Information sources: The Shrinking Aral Sea Recovers http://earthobservatory.nasa.gov/IOTD/view.php?id=46685

Tajikistan is dominated by the Tajiks.[33] Tajikistan is home of the Pamir Mountains and boasts to Central Asia's highest mountain peaks, reaching over 23,000 feet. Political instability and intense winter blizzards that can last for days make travel in the region extremely challenging.[34]

Review Terms

Bolsheviks
Caucasus Mountains
Central Asia
command economy
double landlocked
forward capital
geopolitics
glasnost

heartland theory
Lenin
perestroika
rimland theory
Russia
Russian Core
Russify
Siberia

Transcaucasia
transcontinental
Turkestan
Union of Soviet Socialist
    Republics
Ural Mountains

Research Topics

centrality
Chernobyl
desertification
distance decay
gulag archipelago
human trafficking
Iron Curtain
monocentric
near abroad
new silk road
oligarchy
permafrost
revanchism
russification
satellite state
transhumance
Trans-Siberian Railway

Credits

1. **Source:** From Thomas J. Karwoski, *World Regional Geography: An Introduction*, 1st ed., Copyright © 2016 by Kendall Hunt Publishing Company. Reprinted by permission.
2. **Source:** From Thomas J. Karwoski, *World Regional Geography: An Introduction*, 1st ed., Copyright © 2016 by Kendall Hunt Publishing Company. Reprinted by permission.
3. **Source:** From Thomas J. Karwoski, *World Regional Geography: An Introduction*, 1st ed., Copyright © 2016 by Kendall Hunt Publishing Company. Reprinted by permission.
4. **Source:** From Thomas J. Karwoski, *World Regional Geography: An Introduction*, 1st ed., Copyright © 2016 by Kendall Hunt Publishing Company. Reprinted by permission.
5. **Source:** From Thomas J. Karwoski, *World Regional Geography: An Introduction*, 1st ed., Copyright © 2016 by Kendall Hunt Publishing Company. Reprinted by permission.
6. **Source:** From Thomas J. Karwoski, *World Regional Geography: An Introduction*, 1st ed., Copyright © 2016 by Kendall Hunt Publishing Company. Reprinted by permission.
7. **Source:** From Thomas J. Karwoski, *World Regional Geography: An Introduction*, 1st ed., Copyright © 2016 by Kendall Hunt Publishing Company. Reprinted by permission.
8. **Source:** From Thomas J. Karwoski, *World Regional Geography: An Introduction*, 1st ed., Copyright © 2016 by Kendall Hunt Publishing Company. Reprinted by permission.
9. **Source:** From Thomas J. Karwoski, *World Regional Geography: An Introduction*, 1st ed., Copyright © 2016 by Kendall Hunt Publishing Company. Reprinted by permission.
10. **Source:** From Thomas J. Karwoski, *World Regional Geography: An Introduction*, 1st ed., Copyright © 2016 by Kendall Hunt Publishing Company. Reprinted by permission.
11. **Source:** From Thomas J. Karwoski, *World Regional Geography: An Introduction*, 1st ed., Copyright © 2016 by Kendall Hunt Publishing Company. Reprinted by permission.
12. **Source:** From Thomas J. Karwoski, *World Regional Geography: An Introduction*, 1st ed., Copyright © 2016 by Kendall Hunt Publishing Company. Reprinted by permission.
13. **Source:** From Thomas J. Karwoski, *World Regional Geography: An Introduction*, 1st ed., Copyright © 2016 by Kendall Hunt Publishing Company. Reprinted by permission.

14. **Source:** From Thomas J. Karwoski, *World Regional Geography: An Introduction*, 1st ed., Copyright © 2016 by Kendall Hunt Publishing Company. Reprinted by permission.

15. **Source:** From Thomas J. Karwoski, *World Regional Geography: An Introduction*, 1st ed., Copyright © 2016 by Kendall Hunt Publishing Company. Reprinted by permission.

16. **Source:** From Thomas J. Karwoski, *World Regional Geography: An Introduction*, 1st ed., Copyright © 2016 by Kendall Hunt Publishing Company. Reprinted by permission.

17. **Source:** From Thomas J. Karwoski, *World Regional Geography: An Introduction*, 1st ed., Copyright © 2016 by Kendall Hunt Publishing Company. Reprinted by permission.

18. **Source:** From Thomas J. Karwoski, *World Regional Geography: An Introduction*, 1st ed., Copyright © 2016 by Kendall Hunt Publishing Company. Reprinted by permission.

19. **Source:** From Thomas J. Karwoski, *World Regional Geography: An Introduction*, 1st ed., Copyright © 2016 by Kendall Hunt Publishing Company. Reprinted by permission.

20. **Source:** From Thomas J. Karwoski, *World Regional Geography: An Introduction*, 1st ed., Copyright © 2016 by Kendall Hunt Publishing Company. Reprinted by permission.

21. **Source:** From Thomas J. Karwoski, *World Regional Geography: An Introduction*, 1st ed., Copyright © 2016 by Kendall Hunt Publishing Company. Reprinted by permission.

22. **Source:** From Alan A. Lew, C. Michael Hall, and Dallen J. Timothy, *World Regional Geography: Human Mobilities, Tourism, Destinations, Sustainable Environments*, 2nd ed., Copyright © 2015 by Kendall Hunt Publishing Company. Reprinted by permission.

23. **Source:** From Thomas J. Karwoski, *World Regional Geography: An Introduction*, 1st ed., Copyright © 2016 by Kendall Hunt Publishing Company. Reprinted by permission.

24. **Source:** From Alan A. Lew, C. Michael Hall, and Dallen J. Timothy, *World Regional Geography: Human Mobilities, Tourism, Destinations, Sustainable Environments*, 2nd ed., Copyright © 2015 by Kendall Hunt Publishing Company. Reprinted by permission.

25. **Source:** From Thomas J. Karwoski, *World Regional Geography: An Introduction*, 1st ed., Copyright © 2016 by Kendall Hunt Publishing Company. Reprinted by permission.

26. **Source:** From Alan A. Lew, C. Michael Hall, and Dallen J. Timothy, *World Regional Geography: Human Mobilities, Tourism, Destinations, Sustainable Environments*, 2nd ed., Copyright © 2015 by Kendall Hunt Publishing Company. Reprinted by permission.

27. **Source:** From Thomas J. Karwoski, *World Regional Geography: An Introduction*, 1st ed., Copyright © 2016 by Kendall Hunt Publishing Company. Reprinted by permission.

28. **Source:** From Thomas J. Karwoski, *World Regional Geography: An Introduction*, 1st ed., Copyright © 2016 by Kendall Hunt Publishing Company. Reprinted by permission.

29. **Source:** From Alan A. Lew, C. Michael Hall, and Dallen J. Timothy, *World Regional Geography: Human Mobilities, Tourism, Destinations, Sustainable Environments*, 2nd ed., Copyright © 2015 by Kendall Hunt Publishing Company. Reprinted by permission.

30. **Source:** From Thomas J. Karwoski, *World Regional Geography: An Introduction*, 1st ed., Copyright © 2016 by Kendall Hunt Publishing Company. Reprinted by permission.

31. **Source:** From Thomas J. Karwoski, *World Regional Geography: An Introduction*, 1st ed., Copyright © 2016 by Kendall Hunt Publishing Company. Reprinted by permission.

32. **Source:** From Alan A. Lew, C. Michael Hall, and Dallen J. Timothy, *World Regional Geography: Human Mobilities, Tourism, Destinations, Sustainable Environments*, 2nd ed., Copyright © 2015 by Kendall Hunt Publishing Company. Reprinted by permission.

33. **Source:** From Thomas J. Karwoski, *World Regional Geography: An Introduction*, 1st ed., Copyright © 2016 by Kendall Hunt Publishing Company. Reprinted by permission.

34. **Source:** From Alan A. Lew, C. Michael Hall, and Dallen J. Timothy, *World Regional Geography: Human Mobilities, Tourism, Destinations, Sustainable Environments*, 2nd ed., Copyright © 2015 by Kendall Hunt Publishing Company. Reprinted by permission.

Chapter 7

EAST ASIA

Let her sleep, for when she wakes, she will shake the world.

—Napoleon Bonaparte on China

Where is East Asia?

East Asia refers to a region in the eastern part of Asia.[1] That resides in the Northern and Eastern Hemispheres. The continental land sits mostly on the Eurasian tectonic plate, but some of the islands are divided between the Eurasian and North American tectonic plates, narrowly missing the Philippine tectonic plate.

The East Asian Region

© Olga Turkas/Shutterstock.com

Major Qualities of East Asia

East Asia is the second most populous world region, containing about[2] 21.5 percent of the world population. Only South Asia has more people. China is the most populated country in the world, with about 1.4 billion people.[3] East Asia is racially one of the most homogeneous regions of the world. China is 90.5 percent ethnic Han Chinese, Japan is 98.4 percent Japanese, and Korea is about 99 percent Korean.[4]

A wide spectrum of economic development exists in East Asia. Japan, South Korea, and Taiwan are all highly developed economies. China is one of the fastest growing economies, though still considered less developed. Mongolia is a relatively poor, less developed country. North Korea is one of the most economically poor countries in the world. East Asia is a major part of today's world economy and an emerging center of political power. This chapter focuses primarily on China, with a secondary focus on Japan.[5]

Land and Climate Patterns[6] of China

Eastern and Western China differ in terms of topography, climate, and population. Eastern China is mainly comprised of river and coastal lowlands, while Western China is mainly mountains and high plateaus. Eastern China[7] has a primarily[8] humid temperate climate, whereas Western China is mainly dry[9] and much colder in the winter months, due to its continental[10] location. Eastern China is densely populated, while Western China is sparsely populated.[11] Its location on the Pacific Ring of Fire makes it a key location for seismic activity, and typhoons are also common in the region.

Main Rivers of China

Many rivers flow through China, but two strike with the most importance. The Chang Jiang (the Yangtze) is the principal river of south central China. China's longest river, it is also one of the longest rivers in the world. It originates in the Tibetan Plateau and flows into the East China Sea. Shanghai, China's largest city, lies at its mouth. The Chang Jiang is China's major river for moving goods and people. The **Three Gorges Dam** lies in the central part of the Chang Jiang and is the world's largest hydroelectric dam. It is a multipurpose project, controlling flooding, generating electricity, and improving navigation further into China's interior.

Three Gorges Dam in China, on the Yangtze River.

© Thomas Barrat/Shutterstock.com

The Huang He (the Yellow River) is the main river of North China. It also originates in the Tibetan Plateau, making a big U loop around the Ordos Desert and flowing through the North China Plain before emptying into the Bohai Gulf. The North China Plain is the historic core area of Chinese culture, including the capital city of Beijing.[12]

The Great Wall of China

The Great Wall of China is the country's most recognized cultural icon, and it has much symbolic significance for how China relates to the outside world. It was built to protect China from periodic invasions by nomadic northern tribes. The Great Wall also played a role in keeping China "Chinese" by maintaining cultural uniformity to the south of the wall. In some periods of Chinese history, ethnic Chinese were not allowed to leave China, and they were considered no longer Chinese if they did.[13]

The Great Wall of China.
© aphotostory/Shutterstock.com

Chinese Culture and History

For 4,000 years, a series of dynasties secluded China. The most formative dynasty for Chinese culture is the Han (Qin) dynasty (206 BC to 220 AD). Ethnic Chinese describe themselves as Han Chinese. The last dynasty is the Manchu (Qing) dynasty (1644–1911 AD). It was the most extensive dynasty in area and lasted from the mid-1600s to the early 1900s. In 1911, the last Chinese emperor was replaced during the Japanese invasion.[14]

Chinese Religious Complex

Three main religious philosophies historically influenced China: Buddhism, Confucianism, and Taoism.

Buddhism originated in South Asia and spread extensively through East and Southeast Asia. When Buddhism diffused into China, it intermixed with two native Chinese philosophies, Confucianism and Taoism.

Confucianism is a philosophy that dates from the sixth century BC. It was developed by an early Chinese philosopher, Confucius, and has had a significant influence on Chinese culture. A "behavioral philosophy," it instructs people how to behave toward other people. Confucianism stresses obedience to authority, loyalty to the family, reverence to the elderly, importance of education, and following proper social behavior. It is the basis for the "Asian Way of doing business."

Taoism is an ecological philosophy derived from the teachings of Lao-Tzu. It is rooted in nature worship, respect toward the environment, and mystical healing practices. The concepts of "yin" and "yang" derive from Taoism.[15]

Confucius statue. Located in Fuzi Miao (Confucian Temple), Nanjing, Jiangsu, China.

© aphotostory/Shutterstock.com

Twentieth Century Political Developments

By the 1940s, a full-scale civil war broke out in China between the Communists, led by Mao Zedong, and the nationalists, led by Chang Kai-shek. In 1949, the communists were victorious, and the defeated nationalists fled to the island of Taiwan. Mao formed the People's Republic of China, based on the communist political and economic philosophy.

In the late 1950s and early 1960s, Mao initiated the **Great Leap Forward**. It was an overly ambitious policy to enforce a labor-intensive industrialization at the expense of agriculture. The result was grossly inferior products and a depressed agricultural system. Tens of millions of people died under this repressive and ruthless administration.

From the mid-1960s to the mid-1970s, Mao launched another brutally repressive strategy, the **Cultural Revolution**, a policy to ensure a long-term communist society by using radical young people, known as the **Red Guards**, who attacked parents, lawyers, and teachers to rid China of elite bourgeois elements. People were instructed to dress alike and think alike. The economy suffered, and food and industrial production decreased. Again, tens of millions of people died from torture and starvation. After Mao's death in 1976, China's economy began to recover and eventually become greatly transformed into a rapidly growing economy geared toward exports with global impact.[6]

China's Population Issues

Today China has 1.4 billion people, and is the most populated country in the world. By the mid-twentieth century, China was one of the fastest growing countries, growing by 3 percent per year.

The post-Mao Chinese government realized that China needed to reduce its population growth to ensure future economic growth and adopted the **one-child policy**. By the late 1980s, growth had slowed to 1.2 percent; today the growth is near 0.5 percent. Although successfully reducing population growth, the policy has engendered many negative, unintended consequences. In most Asian cultures, preference has always been in favor of males rather than females. China's one-child policy capitalized on the availability of sonograms, to discover fetal gender. If a female were detected, there is much evidence of its abortion to allow

China abolished its one-child policy concept.

© Crystal Eye Studio/Shutterstock.com

the opportunity of producing another child, preferably male. If the female fetus were not aborted, evidence indicates a lot of female infanticide occurred. If neither abortion nor infanticide happened, many girls were placed in orphanages. The overall result is one of the most unbalanced gender ratios in the world (approximately[17] 115 males per 100 females). Very recently, the Chinese government re-evaluated the policy.[18] The policy is now a **two-child policy**, allowing each couple to have up to two children.

The East Asian Region

East Asia includes the six political entities of China, Mongolia, North Korea, South Korea, Taiwan, and Japan.[19]

China

The core area of China refers to the eastern portion. It is climatically humid, topographically more lowlands, densely populated, and ethnically Han Chinese. It also includes most of the agriculture, industry, and large cities within China.

China today is one of the fastest growing economies of the world. The economic growth is uneven, though. Most economic benefits and successes have primarily occurred in the coastal regions and secondarily in Beijing. In contrast, China's interior and northeast portions have seen little economic expansion.

The Forbidden City in Beijing, China.

© chuyuss/Shutterstock.com

Most of the growth coincides with China's **Special Economic Zones**, which are concentrated along the east coast, especially around Shanghai and on the coast opposite Taiwan and Hong Kong, such as Shenzhen. The Beijing area is another growth core. In these Special Zones, the Chinese government highly encourages foreign investment.

China's **Rust Belt** is in the Northeast China Plain, historically known as Manchuria. Here cities are economically distressed, with many people and industries leaving for the South.[20]

China's Southwest autonomous region, **Tibet**, was conquered in 1950. It is most known for being the home of the Dalai Lama (the Tibetan Buddhist leader) and for its extreme elevations and deep canyons. The people in Tibet have adapted over time to the high altitude, in which less than two percent of people on Earth live.

Mongolia

Mongolia is a sparsely populated, landlocked, and isolated buffer state between China and Russia. Historically, it is the home of the Mongol Empire. Today, it contains a vast array of minerals, such as gold, copper, and coal,[21] and mining is the country's biggest foreign exchange earner.[22] Chinese involvement and economic investment have been growing steadily.[23]

Most of Mongolia is arid with steppe grassland vegetation[24] or desert landscape. It is the home of the Gobi Desert. Its location far from the ocean prevents any benefit from the prevailing onshore summer monsoon winds.[25]

The Potala Palace in Lhasa – Tibet

© Hung Chung Chih/Shutterstock.com

Mongolia's. Gobi Desert.

© Tokareva Irina/Shutterstock.com

North Korea

North Korea occupies the northern half of the Korean peninsula. After World War II, Communists expanded control into the north, whereas non-Communists took over the south. From 1950–1953, the Korean War became an international event between communists and non-communists. A stalemate resulted in an armistice agreement that used the 38th parallel (38 degrees North latitude) as a dividing line, now separating two independent countries: North Korea and South Korea.[26]

Kim Il Sung and Kim Jong Il - Pyongyang, North Korea

© Andreas.Mattsson/Shutterstock.com

Although ethnically one people, North Korea and South Korea are vastly different countries. North Korea is ruled by a dictatorial state communist government that controls all aspects of daily life. It is mountainous with considerable mineral wealth, including coal and iron—keys for heavy manufacturing—yet[27] North Korea is one of the economically poorest and most regimented countries in the world.[28] The supreme leadership of Kim Il-sung, then Kim Jong-il, and now Kim Jong-un, has kept the isolated citizens in abject poverty with extreme malnutrition and even starvation at times.

South Korea

South Korea is one of the most economically developed countries in the world today.

Yurts

One of the most popular international tourist activities in Mongolia is a stay in a yurt (known locally as a *gir*) tent village on the Mongolian steppe. It includes eating traditional food (mutton, camel meat, and fermented horse milk) and riding horses and camels.

A Mongolian nomadic yurt, a safe haven in the harsh desert climate.

© aleksander hunta / Shutterstock.com

Its capital, Seoul, is modern and well developed. A dictatorship in the 1970s, South Korea has become a successful democracy.

South Korea is one of the four **Asian Tigers**. Hong Kong, Singapore, and Taiwan are the other three. These four countries made the rapid[29] economic transformation from the less developed world to the more developed world in the 1960s and 1970s.[30]

While mountainous, South Korea has more lowland area that is suitable for agriculture, than does North Korea. It has a more humid temperate and subtropical climate, which allows for double cropping in its southernmost areas,[32] like parts of south China. North Korea and South Korea are often described as having **regional complementarity**, meaning that each country has what the other lacks.

Taiwan

Taiwan is an island off the east central coast of China. After Mao Zedong led the Chinese communists to defeat Chang Kai-shek in 1949, the nationalists fled to Taiwan. Today, it is a modern, industrial, and well developed state. China still refers to it as a breakaway province, eventually to be reunited with the mainland.[33]

Taiwan, which refers to itself as the Republic of China (ROC) officially considers itself the original China and an independent government, separate from the PRC (People's Republic of China.) Taiwan has one of the highest per capita incomes in Asia, and its capital, Taipei, had the world's tallest building until 2007. Although Taiwan does not have large volcanoes, it is part of the Pacific Ring of Fire and has dramatic mountains that reach over 13,000 feet.[34]

Taipei, Taiwan city skyline at twilight.
© Sean Pavone/Shutterstock.com

Japan

Japan is an island state east of the Korean Peninsula. Four main islands comprise Japan: Hokkaido, Honshu, Kyushu, and Shikoku. Honshu is the largest island in area and population. Tokyo, the capital and largest city, is on this island. Honshu also includes the Tokaido megalopolis, a collection of coalesced metropolitan areas that stretche from Tokyo on the northeast through Yokohama to Osaka, Kobe, and Kyoto on the southwest. Kyoto is the historic cultural center and former capital of Japan. Hiroshima, on the southwest coast, was one of the two Japanese cities upon which the U.S. dropped an atomic bomb.

Wood statue of dragon in Japan
© Taku/Shutterstock.com

Hokkaido is the northernmost of the main Japanese islands. The Ainu, indigenous people of Japan, are mainly concentrated on Hokkaido. Shikoku is the smallest of the main Japanese islands. Kyushu is the southernmost main Japanese island. It includes the city of Nagasaki, the other city devastated by atomic warfare.

Buddhism diffused to Japan from China and Korea. In Japan, Buddhism became intermixed with **Shintoism**, a native Japanese religious philosophy closely bound to Japanese nationalism. It is a place-and nature-centered religion, including beliefs of harmony and balance with nature.

Japan did not emerge as a unified state until the seventh century A.D. and, until the mid-1800s, Japan was a medieval and feudal society. **Shoguns** were local and regional rulers who used warriors, the **samurai**, to enforce their rule. In the 1600s, the most powerful shogun reunited Japan and established it as an isolated state in the Tokugawa Shogunate. In the 1860s, the **Meiji Restoration** brought back the emperor as the monarch of Japan, moved the capital to what is now Tokyo, and initiated a process of modernization and industrialization.

By the early 1900s, Japan was a major global leader in industry and military power. It expanded its control to the Korean Peninsula and invaded Manchuria in the 1930s. In 1941, Japan attacked Pearl Harbor in 1945, in retribution the U.S. dropped the atomic bombs on Hiroshima and Nagasaki.

Although militarily defeated in World War II, Japan arose from physical destruction to become a global leader in industry and economic development by the 1970s and 1980s. Japan lacks major mineral resources, such as coal and oil, which usually lead to development. Japan capitalized on its highly homogeneous, intensely nationalistic population. Japanese workers possessed a high work ethic that, combined with historically low wages, economic production became very profitable. After the end of World War II, the U.S. rewrote the Japanese constitution, promising to defend Japan if necessary. This allowed monies that would have gone to military use to be devoted to improving

Fujiyoshida, Japan at Chureito Pagoda and Mt. Fuji in the spring with cherry blossoms.

© Sean Pavone/Shutterstock.com

Tsunami devastated Fukushima, Japan in April 2011.

© Smallcreative/Shutterstock.com

the economy. The long-term advantage of the war's physical destruction was that Japan rebuilt its economic infrastructure with modern machinery and technology.[35]

Japan's location on the Pacific Rim makes it susceptible to a tremendous amount of tectonic plate activity, including over 1,000 earthquakes a year and numerous volcanoes. Earthquakes can also trigger a **tsunami**, an underwater earthquake that can displace large amounts of sea water extremely quickly, and devastate coastal areas. Part of Japan sits on the Eurasian tectonic plate and part on the North American tectonic plate, rendering Japan's lithosphere to be quite volatile.

Review Terms

Asian Tigers
Buddhism
Confucianism
Cultural Revolution
East Asia
Great Leap Forward
Meiji Restoration

one-child policy
Red Guards
regional complementarity
Rust Belt
samurai
Shintoism
Shoguns

Special Economic Zones
Taoism
Three Gorges Dam
Tibet
tsunami
two-child policy

Research Topics

alluvial fan
autonomous region
Belt and Road Initiative
BRICS
floating population
foreign direct investment
geisha
gender imbalance
high-value-added goods
Hukou system
megacity
silk road
sinicization (Hanification)
state capitalism
techno pole

Credits

1. **Source:** From Thomas J. Karwoski, *World Regional Geography: An Introduction*, 1st ed., Copyright © 2016 by Kendall Hunt Publishing Company. Reprinted by permission.
2. **Source:** From Thomas J. Karwoski, *World Regional Geography: An Introduction*, 1st ed., Copyright © 2016 by Kendall Hunt Publishing Company. Reprinted by permission.
3. **Source:** From Thomas J. Karwoski, *World Regional Geography: An Introduction*, 1st ed., Copyright © 2016 by Kendall Hunt Publishing Company. Reprinted by permission.
4. **Source:** From Alan A. Lew, C. Michael Hall, and Dallen J. Timothy, *World Regional Geography: Human Mobilities, Tourism, Destinations, Sustainable Environments*, 2nd ed., Copyright © 2015 by Kendall Hunt Publishing Company. Reprinted by permission.
5. **Source:** From Thomas J. Karwoski, *World Regional Geography: An Introduction*, 1st ed., Copyright © 2016 by Kendall Hunt Publishing Company. Reprinted by permission.
6. **Source:** From Thomas J. Karwoski, *World Regional Geography: An Introduction*, 1st ed., Copyright © 2016 by Kendall Hunt Publishing Company. Reprinted by permission.
7. **Source:** From Thomas J. Karwoski, *World Regional Geography: An Introduction*, 1st ed., Copyright © 2016 by Kendall Hunt Publishing Company. Reprinted by permission.
8. **Source:** From Thomas J. Karwoski, *World Regional Geography: An Introduction*, 1st ed., Copyright © 2016 by Kendall Hunt Publishing Company. Reprinted by permission.

9. **Source:** From Thomas J. Karwoski, *World Regional Geography: An Introduction*, 1st ed., Copyright © 2016 by Kendall Hunt Publishing Company. Reprinted by permission.
10. **Source:** From Alan A. Lew, C. Michael Hall, and Dallen J. Timothy, *World Regional Geography: Human Mobilities, Tourism, Destinations, Sustainable Environments*, 2nd ed., Copyright © 2015 by Kendall Hunt Publishing Company. Reprinted by permission.
11. **Source:** From Thomas J. Karwoski, *World Regional Geography: An Introduction*, 1st ed., Copyright © 2016 by Kendall Hunt Publishing Company. Reprinted by permission.
12. **Source:** From Thomas J. Karwoski, *World Regional Geography: An Introduction*, 1st ed., Copyright © 2016 by Kendall Hunt Publishing Company. Reprinted by permission.
13. **Source:** From Alan A. Lew, C. Michael Hall, and Dallen J. Timothy, *World Regional Geography: Human Mobilities, Tourism, Destinations, Sustainable Environments*, 2nd ed., Copyright © 2015 by Kendall Hunt Publishing Company. Reprinted by permission.
14. **Source:** From Thomas J. Karwoski, *World Regional Geography: An Introduction*, 1st ed., Copyright © 2016 by Kendall Hunt Publishing Company. Reprinted by permission.
15. **Source:** From Thomas J. Karwoski, *World Regional Geography: An Introduction*, 1st ed., Copyright © 2016 by Kendall Hunt Publishing Company. Reprinted by permission.
16. **Source:** From Thomas J. Karwoski, *World Regional Geography: An Introduction*, 1st ed., Copyright © 2016 by Kendall Hunt Publishing Company. Reprinted by permission.
17. **Source:** From Thomas J. Karwoski, *World Regional Geography: An Introduction*, 1st ed., Copyright © 2016 by Kendall Hunt Publishing Company. Reprinted by permission.
18. **Source:** From Thomas J. Karwoski, *World Regional Geography: An Introduction*, 1st ed., Copyright © 2016 by Kendall Hunt Publishing Company. Reprinted by permission.
19. **Source:** From Thomas J. Karwoski, *World Regional Geography: An Introduction*, 1st ed., Copyright © 2016 by Kendall Hunt Publishing Company. Reprinted by permission.
20. **Source:** From Thomas J. Karwoski, *World Regional Geography: An Introduction*, 1st ed., Copyright © 2016 by Kendall Hunt Publishing Company. Reprinted by permission.
21. **Source:** From Thomas J. Karwoski, *World Regional Geography: An Introduction*, 1st ed., Copyright © 2016 by Kendall Hunt Publishing Company. Reprinted by permission.
22. **Source:** From Alan A. Lew, C. Michael Hall, and Dallen J. Timothy, *World Regional Geography: Human Mobilities, Tourism, Destinations, Sustainable Environments*, 2nd ed., Copyright © 2015 by Kendall Hunt Publishing Company. Reprinted by permission.
23. **Source:** From Thomas J. Karwoski, *World Regional Geography: An Introduction*, 1st ed., Copyright © 2016 by Kendall Hunt Publishing Company. Reprinted by permission.
24. **Source:** From Thomas J. Karwoski, *World Regional Geography: An Introduction*, 1st ed., Copyright © 2016 by Kendall Hunt Publishing Company. Reprinted by permission.
25. **Source:** From Thomas J. Karwoski, *World Regional Geography: An Introduction*, 1st ed., Copyright © 2016 by Kendall Hunt Publishing Company. Reprinted by permission.
26. **Source:** From Thomas J. Karwoski, *World Regional Geography: An Introduction*, 1st ed., Copyright © 2016 by Kendall Hunt Publishing Company. Reprinted by permission.
27. **Source:** From Alan A. Lew, C. Michael Hall, and Dallen J. Timothy, *World Regional Geography: Human Mobilities, Tourism, Destinations, Sustainable Environments*, 2nd ed., Copyright © 2015 by Kendall Hunt Publishing Company. Reprinted by permission.
28. **Source:** From Thomas J. Karwoski, *World Regional Geography: An Introduction*, 1st ed., Copyright © 2016 by Kendall Hunt Publishing Company. Reprinted by permission.
29. **Source:** From Thomas J. Karwoski, *World Regional Geography: An Introduction*, 1st ed., Copyright © 2016 by Kendall Hunt Publishing Company. Reprinted by permission.
30. **Source:** From Thomas J. Karwoski, *World Regional Geography: An Introduction*, 1st ed., Copyright © 2016 by Kendall Hunt Publishing Company. Reprinted by permission.
31. **Source:** From Alan A. Lew, C. Michael Hall, and Dallen J. Timothy, *World Regional Geography: Human Mobilities, Tourism, Destinations, Sustainable Environments*, 2nd ed., Copyright © 2015 by Kendall Hunt Publishing Company. Reprinted by permission.
32. **Source:** From Alan A. Lew, C. Michael Hall, and Dallen J. Timothy, *World Regional Geography: Human Mobilities, Tourism, Destinations, Sustainable Environments*, 2nd ed., Copyright © 2015 by Kendall Hunt Publishing Company. Reprinted by permission.

33. **Source:** From Thomas J. Karwoski, *World Regional Geography: An Introduction*, 1st ed., Copyright © 2016 by Kendall Hunt Publishing Company. Reprinted by permission.
34. **Source:** From Alan A. Lew, C. Michael Hall, and Dallen J. Timothy, *World Regional Geography: Human Mobilities, Tourism, Destinations, Sustainable Environments,* 2nd ed., Copyright © 2015 by Kendall Hunt Publishing Company. Reprinted by permission.
35. **Source:** From Thomas J. Karwoski, *World Regional Geography: An Introduction*, 1st ed., Copyright © 2016 by Kendall Hunt Publishing Company. Reprinted by permission.

Chapter 8

SOUTH ASIA

Violent means will give violent freedom. That would be a menace to the world and to India herself.

—Mahatma Gandhi

Where is South Asia?

South Asia refers to a region located in the south central portion of Asia[1] near the Indian Ocean. Mountains and deserts physically separate it from the rest of the Asian continent. India is the dominant country in area and population within the region. Given the size of the territory and the regional dominance of India, this region is often referred to as the Indian subcontinent.[2] South Asia resides in the Northern and Eastern Hemispheres. The core of the region sits on the Indian tectonic plate (geologically connected to the Australian plate),[3] with the western and eastern edges on the Eurasian tectonic plate.

The South Asian Region.
© PSboom/Shutterstock.com

Major Qualities of South Asia

Currently, South Asia is the most populated world region. It contains[4] almost 25 percent of the world's population. India is the second most populated country in the world, exceeded only by China. South Asia's population is not only large, but it is growing rapidly, raising concerns about whether food production can keep pace with the population growth.

95

South Asia is one of the economically poorest regions in the world. Income levels are low, poverty is widespread, and the standard of living is low. Given the low level of development, subsistence agriculture is the main economic activity. The two dominant countries in the region, India and Pakistan, have been involved in numerous conflicts since their independence in 1947. Both countries have nuclear weapons.[5]

The Monsoon

South Asia's weather and climate are characterized by a monsoon climate. A **monsoon** is defined as a seasonal change in wind direction. It is a phenomenon most evident in South Asia, where a large expanse of land is adjacent to large bodies of water. Land and water heat and cool differently from season to season.

In the summer in South Asia, the Asian landmass quickly and intensely heats. The large mass of warm air, being light, rises and forms an intense low pressure system. At the same time, the Indian Ocean to the south is cooler than the land. The cool air, being heavy and dense, sinks

Indian people travel by boat through the flooded roads in Pathanamthitta, Kerala, India. Kerala was badly affected by the floods during the monsoon (August 2018.)
© AJP/Shutterstock.com

and forms a high pressure system. Wind always flows from high pressure toward low pressure. In the summer, the dominant flow is from the southwest toward the northeast. The summer southwest monsoon brings moisture off the water onto the land. Mountains intensify the effect and cause with it much rainfall, especially in the northeast.

In the winter, conditions are reversed. The Asian landmass quickly and intensely cools, forming high pressure systems. The Indian Ocean is warmer in the winter, forming a low pressure system. Thus, a reverse wind flow occurs. In the winter northeast monsoon, dry conditions result over South Asia.[6]

Landform Patterns

There are four main landform areas in South Asia. The Himalayan Mountains and adjacent mountains dominate in the northeast, while desert landscape is common in the northwest. South of the mountains are the river lowlands. In Pakistan, the Indus River and in north India, the Ganges River are the center of life. The Ganges that connects with the Brahmaputra River from the northeast to form a large delta in Bangladesh. In central India, the Central Indian Plateau is a transition area of hills and rolling topography.

The Deccan Plateau occupies most of southern India. It is a volcanic tableland that descends to the narrow coastal plains below it.[7]

Cultural History

The Dravidians are the native occupants of South Asia. They are darker-skinned people who today inhabit the Deccan Plateau. They speak the Dravidian language, a different language family from most of the rest of South Asia. The Indo-Aryans are lighter-skinned people who came from the northwest around 1500 BC. They introduced the Indo-European languages and the basis for Hinduism into South Asia.[8]

Language Patterns

Indo-European languages are used in northern and western parts of South Asia. Indo-European languages include Hindi (one of[9] twenty-two official languages of India), Punjabi (on the border of India and Pakistan), Urdu (a traditional language of Pakistan),[10] Dari (also known as Farsi, one of the official Persian languages of Afghanistan), Maldivian (the official language of The Maldives, and Bengali (along the India and Bangladesh border). Dravidian languages are spoken in the Deccan Plateau. Tamil is a major language in southeast India and northern Sri Lanka.[11]

Religious Patterns

Hinduism is the main religion in India and Nepal. Buddhism is the main religion in Sri Lanka and is the state religion in Bhutan. Islam is the dominant religion in[12] Afghanistan, Pakistan, and Bangladesh. Sikhism is practiced in the Punjab area of western India.

Hinduism is considered by many scholars to be the oldest major world religion. It is not just a religion, but a culture, society, and religion interconnected. It is a

Mt. Everest

Mt. Everest is the highest mountain peak in the world, at an elevation of 29,029 feet above sea level. It is one of fifty peaks over 20,000 feet in the vast Himalayas.

Mount Everest and the Khumbu Valley that leads to it are one of the most trekked regions in South Asia. This is the home of the Sherpas, who originally migrated to Nepal from Tibet. Edmund Hillary and Tenzing Norgay first climbed Everest in 1953. Today, some 500 people a year typically attempt the peak, though harsh climate prevents many from achieving their goal, and several die each year in the attempt.

Mt. Everest base camp - Nepal

© Daniel Prudek / Shutterstock.com

complete way of life for its adherents with the Ganges River as a major sacred space for Hinduism. It has no common creed, no single doctrine, and no identifiable single founder. Hinduism is an ethnic, polytheistic, eastern religion. Three main ideas are the essence of the Hindu religion. **Karma** refers to the Hindu belief that a person's soul or spirit can be transferred after the death of the body. Karma also refers to the Hindu belief that the past affects the present, which affects the future. **Reincarnation** is the Hindu belief that, at death, the soul or spirit can be reborn in another form.

The **caste system**, a rigid hierarchy of social classes, is a traditional component of Hindu belief.[13] Some scholars argue that these castes were not clearly fixed hierarchy in India until the late 1800s, when the British shaped them

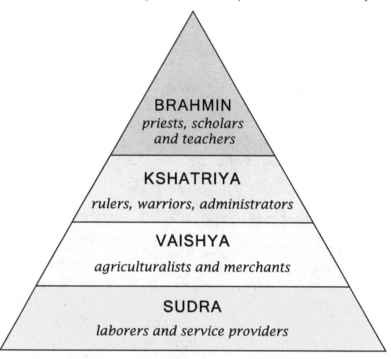

Varna system (Hinduism)

BRAHMIN
priests, scholars and teachers

KSHATRIYA
rulers, warriors, administrators

VAISHYA
agriculturalists and merchants

SUDRA
laborers and service providers

UNTOUCHABLE
tanners, laundresses, tanners, laundresses

The scheme of the historical division of society into Varna (Hinduism). The pyramid of the caste system.

© WindVector/Shutterstock.com

to more resemble the class system to which they were accustomed. The caste system was officially abolished in the 1950 Indian constitution, and many urban Indians today pay little heed to it. However, it continues to be an important influential force within the more traditional rural areas of India. Although frequently criticized, it has had the influence of uniting the great ethnic diversity of India, as caste designation transcends ethnic and language differences.[14]

Buddhism is a major world religion that, like Hinduism, originated in the Ganges River area of northern India. Its founder, Siddhartha Gautama, was born a Hindu prince. He later rejected his princely status and founded a new religion. From its beginnings, Buddhism rejected the caste system. Buddhism is the third main global universalizing religion. The essence of Buddhism is tied to the **Four Noble Truths**. The first truth is the belief that life involves sorrow and suffering. The second truth is that the cause of sorrow and suffering is human desire. People suffer because they want things they cannot have. The third truth is that one can escape suffering by ending desire, stop wanting, and reach a stage of not wanting. The fourth truth is the belief that, to end desire, one must follow a middle path, avoiding extremes of too much pleasure and desire and too much asceticism. This middle path includes meditation and contemplation. Two main spatial branches of Buddhism have evolved. Mahayana Buddhism spread northward to China, Korea, and Japan. Theravada Buddhism spread south and east to Sri Lanka and Southeast Asia.

Islam originated in Southwest Asia, and a group of adherents, the Mughals, arrived in South Asia around 700 A.D. and introduced Islam. For about 1,000 years, they controlled most of this region. Their greatest landscape impact is the Taj Mahal, built by a Mughal prince as a tomb for his deceased wife. Today, Islam is practised in[15] Afghanistan, Pakistan, and Bangladesh and forms the largest religious minority in India. Islam and Hinduism are largely incompatible. Islam is monotheistic, universalizing, does not condone idols, has one sacred book (the Quran), a uniform dogma (The Five Pillars of Faith), eats beef, buries their dead, and theoretically teaches social equality. In contrast, Hinduism is polytheistic, ethnic, reveres many idols, has various sacred writings, varying beliefs, venerates cows, cremates the dead, and includes the rigid caste system.

Buddha statue used as Amulets of Buddhism religion.

© mai111/Shutterstock.com

Sikhism is a hybrid, blended religion that originated in and is popular in the western Indian state of Punjab. The Punjab is a transitional area that lies astride the India/Pakistan border. Pakistan is dry and mountainous, whereas India is humid and more lowland in nature. Islam dominates Pakistan, and Hinduism dominates India. In the 1400s, Sikhism arose in

Women volunteers collectively making "roti" during a Langar or community kitchen service, which in Sikhism refers to free meal for all. Kolkata, India (November 2014.)

© arindambanerjee/Shutterstock.com

the Punjab to try to bring together these two major disparate religions. Sikhism incorporates elements of Hinduism and Islam. Like Hinduism, Sikhs believe in reincarnation. Like Islam, Sikhs are monotheists. The most sacred space for Sikhism is the Golden Temple at Amritsar, the capital of Punjab.[16]

Geopolitical Framework

The Mughal Empire controlled most of South Asia up to the 1700s. By then, the empire had weakened, and political and ethnic tensions emerged. In the power vacuum, a private British company, The British East India Company, assumed political and economic control. In the mid-1800s, a mutiny against the East India Company directly brought in British troops and the British government. During British control, Hindu, Muslim, and Sikh rulers retained much local authority. By the 1920s, political protests began to call for eventual independence. In the 1930s, a charismatic Hindu, **Mahatma Gandhi**, used a campaign of nonviolence to galvanize much of the opposition to the British.

Vintage British East India Company Nautical Typography

© Oleg Iatsun/Shutterstock.com

Mahatma Gandhi (1869–1948)

© Darvik Design/Shutterstock.com

In 1947, the British decided to leave their Indian empire. An agreement called for two new states to emerge, Pakistan and India. It was agreed that the existing pattern of religion would be the basis for the split. Areas with majority Hindus would become India. Areas with majority Muslims would become Pakistan. At the time, Muslims were concentrated in two separate places, to the west and to the east of India. Thus, Pakistan began as a fragmented state, with two parts: West Pakistan and East Pakistan. The capital was in West Pakistan. India would not allow any movement between the two parts of Pakistan across India. Increasingly, people in East Pakistan became isolated from West Pakistan. In the early 1970s, **East Pakistan** seceded from **West Pakistan** and became the independent country of Bangladesh. West Pakistan became the Republic of Pakistan.[17]

The South Asian Region

South Asia is comprised of the states of[18] Afghanistan, Pakistan, India, Bangladesh, Nepal, Bhutan,[19] the Maldives, and Sri Lanka.[20]

Afghanistan

Afghanistan is mainly made up of Indo-European speaking peoples and is a multinational state. The largest ethnic group, the Pushtuns, dominate the south. The Tajiks are the second largest group, in the northeast. The Hazaras live in the central area west of Kabul, the capital. The Uzbeks are the fourth largest group, living in the north.[21]

Marketplace in Kabul, Afghanistan where people can buy and sell birds in cages.

© Michal Knitl/Shutterstock.com

Afghanistan is a largely mountainous country in its eastern portions, with lower lands in its western and southern portions. The major mountain range in Afghanistan is the Hindu Kush (easily accessible from nearly Pakistan. Afghanistan has always been the crossroads between Central and South Asia and between Europe and China. Because of its strategic importance, it has long been sought by imperial powers.[22]

Until the 1970s, Afghanistan was a monarchy. In the late 1970s, a Soviet-supported military revolutionary council seized power and created a Marxist government. To support the Marxist council, Soviet troops invaded in 1979. The Muslim opposition, the mujahideen, became supported by the U.S. and the Saudis. In 1989, the Soviets were forced to withdraw. In the resulting power vacuum, the **Taliban**, a group of young militant Muslim religious students, associated with the Pushtun ethnic group, emerged. This group imposed an extreme interpretation of Islamic law, denying women formal education and forcing them to remain obediently indoors and subservient to men. Other Afghan groups began to oppose the harsh rule of the Taliban. Derived from the Taliban, another radical group emerged, **Al-Qaeda**. It was led by a former Saudi citizen who fought with the mujaheedin against the Soviets, named Osama bin Laden. It was Al-Qaeda who claimed responsibility for the 9/11 attack on U.S. soil. In retaliation, the U.S. and Britain invaded Afghanistan and removed the Taliban from political control. Events in Iraq distracted the U.S., and the Taliban regrouped into the mountains, became more sophisticated with weaponry, and reemerged as a power force in Afghanistan.[23]

Pakistan

Pakistan is an Islamic republic, Consisting of 80 percent Sunni Muslims, and with Shiite Muslims comprising of the rest of the population. Originally, Pakistan included present-day Bangladesh, which became independent in the early 1970s. The traditional capital was the large port city of Karachi. Relatively recently, the capital was relocated to a new forward capital, Islamabad. Islamabad is located in the northern interior, close to an embattled transitional area along the Pakistan–India–China border known as **Kashmir**,[24] which is an autonomous territory. Pakistan is divided into five main provinces. The Punjab province is the wealthiest and most populated in Pakistan.[25]

When partition occurred in 1947, existing states were given the choice of being incorporated into India or Pakistan. In Kashmir, the great majority of the population was Muslim, but the local ruler was Hindu. When he decided not to join

The Wazir Khan Mosque, located in the walled city of Lahore, capital of the Pakistani province of Punjab.

© W_NAMKET/Shutterstock.com

Pakistan, a Muslim uprising, with Pakistan's support, occurred. The local ruler called for help from India. Eventually a ceasefire line was drawn, with most of the territory in India's control. Pakistan has always demanded a referendum, so that people could decide to be in India or Pakistan, but India has refused such a referendum. Both countries have been in conflict over Kashmir several times since 1947. Complicating factors today are that both India and Pakistan have nuclear capabilities, and China also claims part of the Kashmir area. Much of the northwest area of Pakistan is controlled by the Taliban, who support Al-Qaeda. This was the part of Pakistan where Osama bin Laden was captured and killed.[26]

India

India is the main country in South Asia, with over[27] 1.3 billion people and encompassing about 75 percent of the total area. It is currently the second largest country in the world. By 2030, it will likely surpass China to become the most populated world state. It is a political democracy; in fact, India is the most populous democracy in the world.

Mumbai, on the west central coast, is India's largest industrial and financial city. It is also home to "Bollywood," India's equivalent of Hollywood. The Indian entertainment industry is a major element of the city's economy. Mumbai is the key city in India's west.

The Taj Majal mausoleum, an example of Mughal architecture.

© xdrew/Shutterstock.com

New Delhi is India's capital city, located within the vast Ganges River Valley in the north of the country. The Delhi-New Delhi area is India's largest urban concentration. **Varanasi** (Benares) is India's holiest city, one of the world's oldest living cities, and[28] the most single important pilgrimage destination for all sects of Hinduism.[29] It is located along the north bank of the Ganges River where numerous temples are devoted to various Hindu gods. Bangalore, in the southern Deccan Plateau, is the center of India's high-tech computer industry. Kolkata (Calcutta) is India's key city in the east.[30]

The Sadhu Baba (monk) Nondo Somendrah, in Varanasi, India.

© Ruslan Kalnitsky/Shutterstock.com

Bangladesh

Bangladesh was born as an independent country in 1971, following secession from Pakistan,[31] when it was known as East. Pakistan. Bangladesh is one of the most densely populated countries in the world, and its warm climate and ready availability of water allow the growing of three rice crops per year. It occupies the[32] **double delta** of the combined Ganges and Brahmaputra Rivers.[33] Almost half of the country is flooded every year by the two rivers, as well as by tidal floods caused by typhoons from the **Bay of Bengal**, the largest bay in the world. It's capital, Dhaka, sits on wetlands along the Ganges River and is prone to floods especially during the monsoon season.

Much of the country is low-lying, and it is regarded as being extremely susceptible to climate change and sea-level rise. Transportation is a problem because water is everywhere. The country's population is over 80 percent Muslim and has suffered as other largely Islamic populated nations have from perceived security concerns.[34]

Chaung Tha village is located between the Bay of Bengal and Kangy river. The fishing boats stand on the ground in the low tide, in Myanmar.

© eFesenko/Shutterstock.com

Nepal

Nepal is a buffer state between China to the north and India to the south. It is mainly Hindu, with Hinduism as the country's official religion. Nepal is located in the Himalaya Mountains[35] and has existed as a kingdom centered in the Kathmandu Valley for more than 1,500 years. It has nine of the fourteen highest peaks in the world, including Mount Everest.

In recent decades, Nepal has suffered from a **Maoist**-based (a form of Chinese communism) insurgency that controlled most of the rural countryside, while the central government controlled the cities. Many thousands of Nepalese died in the struggle between the two groups. Peace agreements in 2006 brought Maoists into the government and significantly reduced the influence of the monarchy.[36]

Patan, ancient city in Kathmandu Valley Nepal
© Skreidzeleu/Shutterstock.com

Bhutan

Bhutan is another mountainous[37] buffer state[38] wedged between India and China's Tibet area. Buddhism is the official religion of Bhutan.[39] Various Buddhist sects fought for political control for many centuries until the 17th century, when a theocratic government united the country. From that time until 1907, the Kingdom of Bhutan (Druk Yul – Land of the Thunder Dragon) had a system of shared civil and spiritual rule under an absolute monarchy (the Dragon King). The monarchy had traditionally been absolute, although democratic elections

Taktshang Goemba, Tiger Nest Monastery, Bhutan
© Khanthachai C/Shutterstock.com

occurred for the first time in history in December 2007 and March 2008. The king is admired and respected, unlike the King of Nepal, who was largely despised by the people.[40]

Sri Lanka

Sri Lanka is an island state off the southeast coast of India. There are two main ethnic groups that comprise the population of Sri Lanka: the Sinhalese and the Tamils. The Sinhalese are the majority group. Their ancestry lies in northwestern India. They speak an Indo-European language, Sinhala and are religiously Buddhist. The Tamils are the minority group. They came from southern India. They speak Tamil, a Dravidian language, and are religiously Hindu. They are concentrated in the northern and northeastern parts of the island.

A civil war started between these two groups in the mid-1980s. Traditionally, the Buddhist Sinhalese discriminated against the minority Tamils. The majority Sinhalese government finally defeated the radical Tamil Tigers around 2009.[41] Historically, SriLanka was the British colony known as **Ceylon**.

On December 26, 2004, an Indian Ocean tsunami disaster killed more than 30,000 Sri Lankans and devastated the beach resorts of the island. Recovery has been quick, and many of them have since been rebuilt.[42]

Sunrise in the jungles of Sri Lanka.

© Sergieiev/Shutterstock.com

The Maldives[43]

The Maldives consists of some 1,200 coral islands, grouped in a chain of 27 **atolls**[44] (coral reef, island, or islets typically with a lagoon). These coral atolls have live coral and sand bars that sit atop an undersea mountain range southeast of the Indian peninsula. The rising sea level threatens the future of the Maldives, as it threatens other low-lying islands throughout the world, because the highest elevation is only 7.2 feet above sea level. The Maldives has a

Amazing bird eye view in the Maldives.

© Siraphob Werakijpanich/Shutterstock.com

population of about[45] 436,000, is a primarily Muslim country, and another former British colony.[46] It sits at the edge of the Arabian Sea in the Indian Ocean, with its capital Male' near the center of the islands. Its is a top destination for tourists coming to the region.

Review Terms

Al-Qaeda	Hinduism	reincarnation
atolls	India	Sikhism
Bay of Bengal	Karma	South Asia
caste system	Kashmir	Taliban
Ceylon	Mahatma Gandhi	Varanasi
double delta	Maoist	West Pakistan
East Pakistan	monsoon	
Four Noble Truths	Mt. Everest	

Research Topics

British East India Company
bustee
communal tension
demographic burden
Dravidian languages
Indian Diaspora
indirect rule
Jainism
linguistic nationalism
maharaja
partition
physiologic density
population density
population pyramid
transmigration

Credits

1. **Source:** From Thomas J. Karwoski, *World Regional Geography: An Introduction,* 1st ed., Copyright © 2016 by Kendall Hunt Publishing Company. Reprinted by permission.
2. **Source:** From Thomas J. Karwoski, *World Regional Geography: An Introduction,* 1st ed., Copyright © 2016 by Kendall Hunt Publishing Company. Reprinted by permission.
3. **Source:** From Thomas J. Karwoski, *World Regional Geography: An Introduction,* 1st ed., Copyright © 2016 by Kendall Hunt Publishing Company. Reprinted by permission.
4. **Source:** From Thomas J. Karwoski, *World Regional Geography: An Introduction,* 1st ed., Copyright © 2016 by Kendall Hunt Publishing Company. Reprinted by permission.
5. **Source:** From Thomas J. Karwoski, *World Regional Geography: An Introduction,* 1st ed., Copyright © 2016 by Kendall Hunt Publishing Company. Reprinted by permission.
6. **Source:** From Thomas J. Karwoski, *World Regional Geography: An Introduction,* 1st ed., Copyright © 2016 by Kendall Hunt Publishing Company. Reprinted by permission.
7. **Source:** From Thomas J. Karwoski, *World Regional Geography: An Introduction,* 1st ed., Copyright © 2016 by Kendall Hunt Publishing Company. Reprinted by permission.
8. **Source:** From Thomas J. Karwoski, *World Regional Geography: An Introduction,* 1st ed., Copyright © 2016 by Kendall Hunt Publishing Company. Reprinted by permission.

9. **Source:** From Thomas J. Karwoski, *World Regional Geography: An Introduction,* 1st ed., Copyright © 2016 by Kendall Hunt Publishing Company. Reprinted by permission.

10. **Source:** From Thomas J. Karwoski, *World Regional Geography: An Introduction,* 1st ed., Copyright © 2016 by Kendall Hunt Publishing Company. Reprinted by permission.

11. **Source:** From Thomas J. Karwoski, *World Regional Geography: An Introduction,* 1st ed., Copyright © 2016 by Kendall Hunt Publishing Company. Reprinted by permission.

12. **Source:** From Thomas J. Karwoski, *World Regional Geography: An Introduction,* 1st ed., Copyright © 2016 by Kendall Hunt Publishing Company. Reprinted by permission.

13. **Source:** From Thomas J. Karwoski, *World Regional Geography: An Introduction,* 1st ed., Copyright © 2016 by Kendall Hunt Publishing Company. Reprinted by permission.

14. **Source:** From Alan A. Lew, C. Michael Hall, and Dallen J. Timothy, *World Regional Geography: Human Mobilities, Tourism, Destinations, Sustainable Environments*, 2nd ed., Copyright © 2015 by Kendall Hunt Publishing Company. Reprinted by permission.

15. **Source:** From Thomas J. Karwoski, *World Regional Geography: An Introduction,* 1st ed., Copyright © 2016 by Kendall Hunt Publishing Company. Reprinted by permission.

16. **Source:** From Thomas J. Karwoski, *World Regional Geography: An Introduction,* 1st ed., Copyright © 2016 by Kendall Hunt Publishing Company. Reprinted by permission.

17. **Source:** From Thomas J. Karwoski, *World Regional Geography: An Introduction,* 1st ed., Copyright © 2016 by Kendall Hunt Publishing Company. Reprinted by permission.

18. **Source:** From Thomas J. Karwoski, *World Regional Geography: An Introduction,* 1st ed., Copyright © 2016 by Kendall Hunt Publishing Company. Reprinted by permission.

19. **Source:** From Thomas J. Karwoski, *World Regional Geography: An Introduction,* 1st ed., Copyright © 2016 by Kendall Hunt Publishing Company. Reprinted by permission.

20. **Source:** From Thomas J. Karwoski, *World Regional Geography: An Introduction,* 1st ed., Copyright © 2016 by Kendall Hunt Publishing Company. Reprinted by permission.

21. **Source:** From Thomas J. Karwoski, *World Regional Geography: An Introduction,* 1st ed., Copyright © 2016 by Kendall Hunt Publishing Company. Reprinted by permission.

22. **Source:** From Thomas J. Karwoski, *World Regional Geography: An Introduction,* 1st ed., Copyright © 2016 by Kendall Hunt Publishing Company. Reprinted by permission.

23. **Source:** From Thomas J. Karwoski, *World Regional Geography: An Introduction,* 1st ed., Copyright © 2016 by Kendall Hunt Publishing Company. Reprinted by permission.

24. **Source:** From Thomas J. Karwoski, *World Regional Geography: An Introduction,* 1st ed., Copyright © 2016 by Kendall Hunt Publishing Company. Reprinted by permission.

25. **Source:** From Thomas J. Karwoski, *World Regional Geography: An Introduction,* 1st ed., Copyright © 2016 by Kendall Hunt Publishing Company. Reprinted by permission.

26. **Source:** From Thomas J. Karwoski, *World Regional Geography: An Introduction,* 1st ed., Copyright © 2016 by Kendall Hunt Publishing Company. Reprinted by permission.

27. **Source:** From Thomas J. Karwoski, *World Regional Geography: An Introduction,* 1st ed., Copyright © 2016 by Kendall Hunt Publishing Company. Reprinted by permission.

28. **Source:** From Thomas J. Karwoski, *World Regional Geography: An Introduction,* 1st ed., Copyright © 2016 by Kendall Hunt Publishing Company. Reprinted by permission.

29. **Source:** From Alan A. Lew, C. Michael Hall, and Dallen J. Timothy, *World Regional Geography: Human Mobilities, Tourism, Destinations, Sustainable Environments*, 2nd ed., Copyright © 2015 by Kendall Hunt Publishing Company. Reprinted by permission.

30. **Source:** From Thomas J. Karwoski, *World Regional Geography: An Introduction,* 1st ed., Copyright © 2016 by Kendall Hunt Publishing Company. Reprinted by permission.

31. **Source:** From Thomas J. Karwoski, *World Regional Geography: An Introduction,* 1st ed., Copyright © 2016 by Kendall Hunt Publishing Company. Reprinted by permission.

32. **Source:** From Thomas J. Karwoski, *World Regional Geography: An Introduction,* 1st ed., Copyright © 2016 by Kendall Hunt Publishing Company. Reprinted by permission.

33. **Source:** From Thomas J. Karwoski, *World Regional Geography: An Introduction,* 1st ed., Copyright © 2016 by Kendall Hunt Publishing Company. Reprinted by permission.

34. **Source:** From Alan A. Lew, C. Michael Hall, and Dallen J. Timothy, *World Regional Geography: Human Mobilities, Tourism, Destinations, Sustainable Environments*, 2nd ed., Copyright © 2015 by Kendall Hunt Publishing Company. Reprinted by permission.

35. **Source:** From Thomas J. Karwoski, *World Regional Geography: An Introduction*, 1st ed., Copyright © 2016 by Kendall Hunt Publishing Company. Reprinted by permission.

36. **Source:** From Alan A. Lew, C. Michael Hall, and Dallen J. Timothy, *World Regional Geography: Human Mobilities, Tourism, Destinations, Sustainable Environments*, 2nd ed., Copyright © 2015 by Kendall Hunt Publishing Company. Reprinted by permission.

37. **Source:** From Thomas J. Karwoski, *World Regional Geography: An Introduction*, 1st ed., Copyright © 2016 by Kendall Hunt Publishing Company. Reprinted by permission.

38. **Source:** From Alan A. Lew, C. Michael Hall, and Dallen J. Timothy, *World Regional Geography: Human Mobilities, Tourism, Destinations, Sustainable Environments*, 2nd ed., Copyright © 2015 by Kendall Hunt Publishing Company. Reprinted by permission.

39. **Source:** From Thomas J. Karwoski, *World Regional Geography: An Introduction*, 1st ed., Copyright © 2016 by Kendall Hunt Publishing Company. Reprinted by permission.

40. **Source:** From Alan A. Lew, C. Michael Hall, and Dallen J. Timothy, *World Regional Geography: Human Mobilities, Tourism, Destinations, Sustainable Environments*, 2nd ed., Copyright © 2015 by Kendall Hunt Publishing Company. Reprinted by permission.

41. **Source:** From Thomas J. Karwoski, *World Regional Geography: An Introduction*, 1st ed., Copyright © 2016 by Kendall Hunt Publishing Company. Reprinted by permission.

42. **Source:** From Alan A. Lew, C. Michael Hall, and Dallen J. Timothy, *World Regional Geography: Human Mobilities, Tourism, Destinations, Sustainable Environments*, 2nd ed., Copyright © 2015 by Kendall Hunt Publishing Company. Reprinted by permission.

43. **Source:** From Thomas J. Karwoski, *World Regional Geography: An Introduction*, 1st ed., Copyright © 2016 by Kendall Hunt Publishing Company. Reprinted by permission.

44. **Source:** From Alan A. Lew, C. Michael Hall, and Dallen J. Timothy, *World Regional Geography: Human Mobilities, Tourism, Destinations, Sustainable Environments*, 2nd ed., Copyright © 2015 by Kendall Hunt Publishing Company. Reprinted by permission.

45. **Source:** From Alan A. Lew, C. Michael Hall, and Dallen J. Timothy, *World Regional Geography: Human Mobilities, Tourism, Destinations, Sustainable Environments*, 2nd ed., Copyright © 2015 by Kendall Hunt Publishing Company. Reprinted by permission.

46. **Source:** From Alan A. Lew, C. Michael Hall, and Dallen J. Timothy, *World Regional Geography: Human Mobilities, Tourism, Destinations, Sustainable Environments*, 2nd ed., Copyright © 2015 by Kendall Hunt Publishing Company. Reprinted by permission.

Chapter 9

SOUTHEAST ASIA

Where is Southeast Asia?

Southeast Asia is a region that occupies the southeastern part of Asia. Southeast Asia includes both a mainland and insular subregion.[1] The southeast region resides in the Eastern Hemisphere but is dissected by the equator, so it is in both the Northern and Southern Hemispheres. The region is known for dynamic tectonic plate activity, as it sits on three major tectonic plates: Eurasian, Australian, and Indian, and is influenced by three minor tectonic plates: Philippine, Caroline, and Burma.

The Southeast Asian Region

© Alesandro14/Shutterstock.com

Major Qualities of Southeast Asia

Southeast Asia is a physically fragmented region of numerous peninsulas and islands. It is also a culturally fragmented area with various ethnicities, languages, and religions. Similar to Eastern Europe, Southeast Asia exhibits the characteristics of a **shatter belt**, with internal and external factors causing a splintering and fracturing of the region. European, American, Chinese, and Indian influences are evident throughout the region, as are political instability and conflict.[2] The diversity of economies in Southeast Asia today include some of the wealthiest countries in the world (Singapore and Brunei) and some of the poorest (East Timor, Laos, Myanmar and Cambodia), as well as an emerging economy (Malaysia.)[3]

Compared to South and East Asia, Southeast Asia has a relatively low population density. Its estimated population in[4] 2019 was about[5] 661 million, half the total population of India and of China.[6] Indonesia is the dominant country in terms of area and population, being the world's fourth most populated country.[7] About[8] 22 percent of the population of

Southeast Asia lives on the Indonesian island of Java, which is among the most densely populated places in the world.[9] The rest of the Southeast Asia[10] region has a relatively low population density.[11] The region's physical geography features high relief, crustal instability (part of the Pacific Ring of Fire), and tropical climates. Structurally, Southeast Asia includes a mainland subregion and an insular subregion.[12]

Orangutans

One of the most critically endangered mammals is the orangutan. Orangutans once roamed throughout Southeast Asia but today are found in the rainforests of Borneo and Sumatra and in the homes of people throughout Asia who adopt infant orangutans as pets. They are known for their reddish-brown hair and incredible high level of intelligence, and they are becoming increasingly rare in the wild. While cute and cuddly as infants, they can easily toss a human across a room by adulthood.[13]

Male orangutan sitting on a platform in Gunung Leuser National Park, Sumatra, Indonesia. Sumatran orangutan is endemic to the north of Sumatra and is critically endangered.

© Don Mammoser/Shutterstock.com

Physical Geography of[14] Southeast Asia

The mainland subregion[15] consists of countries directly attached to the Asian continent[16] in a series of rugged uplands interspersed with broad river lowlands. Four major rivers dominate the Mainland: the Irrawaddy, Chao Phraya, Mekong, and Red. The Irrawaddy River flows through the country of Myanmar (Burma) in a wide valley, with the largest city of Yangon in its broad delta. The Chao Phraya River flows through the country of Thailand, including the capital and largest city of Bangkok. The Mekong River originates in China, flows

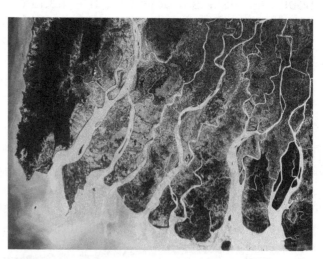

River delta of the Irrawady, a river that flows from north to south through Myanmar.

© lavizzara/Shutterstock.com

along the border of Thailand and Laos, through the middle of Cambodia (including the capital Phnom Penh), and finally ends in a wide delta in southern Vietnam. The Red River also originates in China and flows through the lowland of northern Vietnam, including the capital of Hanoi.[17]

The insular subregion consists of a large arc of volcanic islands formed by the collision of tectonic plates.[18] The subregion has over 26,000 islands, with thousands that are uninhabited and many that do not have individual names. In the middle of this arc is the island of Borneo, which is politically divided among three countries. Part of the Asian landmas Borneo is not geologically volcanic and is the[19] third-largest island in the world.[20] The insular subregion has a vast network of gulfs, seas, and straits that isolate these islands from each other and to their great cultural diversity.

The Wallace Line

The tropical rainforests of Indonesia are home to the second greatest terrestrial biodiversity in the world after Brazil's Amazon rainforest. Its flora and fauna are a mix of Asian and Australian species. The line between these species, known as the **Wallace Line** (after British naturalist Alfred Wallace who first described it), runs roughly between the islands of Borneo and Sulawesi and between Bali and Lombok in southern Indonesia. The Wallace Line follows a deepwater trench between the Asian and Australian continental landmasses that many animals could not cross when sea levels were lower during the ice ages.[21]

Southeast Asia as a Shatter Belt

A large variety of different ethnic and language groups internally fractured and shattered the region of Southeast Asia. These groups include the Thai, Tibetan-Burmese, Vietnamese, Mon-Khmer, Indonesian, and Chinese. This array of varied groups has created a complex ethnic mosaic.

Southeast Asia is also religiously diverse. Buddhism is prevalent throughout most of mainland Southeast Asia. Confucianism is highly present and influential in Vietnam. Islam is practical in Malaysia,[22] Brunei, and Indonesia. Roman Catholicism is the norm in The Philippines[23] and East Timor.

External factors also shatteres and fragment the region. The mainland part of Southeast Asia is often referred to as **Indochina**, referring to the vast influence of South Asians from the west and the Chinese from the north. The first major South Asian influence arrived about 2,000 years ago. Art, music, and religion diffused into Southeast Asia, including early influences of Hinduism. The second wave brought Buddhism in the thirteenth century AD. The Chinese influence was mainly through migration, especially in Vietnam.

A diversity of European political colonialization shattered and fragmented Southeast Asia. The British had colonies in Burma (now Myanmar), Malaya (now Malaysia), and Singapore. The French had a colonial empire including Laos, Cambodia, and Vietnam (French Indochina). The Dutch controlled the Dutch East Indies (now Indonesia). The Spanish controlled the Philippines until 1898, when the U.S. took control after the Spanish-American War ended. The Philippines where under U.S. political control from

1898–1946. Thailand was the only Southeast Asian country not under European or U.S. colonial control.[24]

Territorial Shapes

Southeast Asia is an ideal world area to investigate the different types of political territory that exist. Five main territorial shapes are commonly identified: compact, elongated, protruded, fragmented, and perforated.

A **compact state** has a fairly regular visual shape, such as circular or square or rectangular. Compact states have advantages of easier interconnections within the area and better opportunities to politically control the territory. In Southeast Asia, Cambodia is a classic example of such a compact state. Other global examples include Uruguay, Zimbabwe, Hungary, Slovakia, and Mongolia.

An **elongated state** has a long, narrow shape and faces the potential chal-

The Spanish American War (April-August 1898).

© Everett Historical/Shutterstock.com

lenge of effectively managing and controlling a vast elongated territory. Most elongated states extend north and south, often covering different climate areas over a latitudinal range. In Southeast Asia, Vietnam and Laos are classic examples. Other global examples include Chile, Mozambique, Norway, Sweden, Finland, and Italy.

A **protruded state** is a country whose shape combines compact and elongated features. Much of the territory is relatively compact, but has is at least one elongated section (the protrusion) that presents the potential of isolation and disconnection between the protruded area and the rest of the state. In Southeast Asia, Myanmar and Thailand are classic examples of protruded states. Other global examples include Colombia, Namibia, and Italy.

A **fragmented state** is a country comprised of parts that are physically separated, such as a group of islands or a mainland with separated sections apart from the mainland. Fragmented states have many potential problems in effectively controlling and communicating with the separated parts. In Southeast Asia, The Philippines and Indonesia are classic island example while Malaysia is an example of a country where part of the state is on a peninsula and the other is island. Other global examples include the U.S., Argentina, Chile, Denmark, Italy, Greece, and Japan.

A **perforated state**, or sometimes called an enclaved state, is a country that completely surrounds another country, as if the territory has a perforation, or opening. In Southeast Asia, Indonesia is now a perforated state, with the eastern part of the island of Timor's[25] becoming the country of East Timor in 2002. Other global examples include Italy and South Africa.[26]

Subregions of Southeast Asia

Southeast Asia includes the mainland subregion and the insular subregion.[27]

Mainland

Mainland Southeast Asia is comprised of five states: Myanmar, Thailand, Laos, Cambodia, and Vietnam. These countries are all located on the southeastern mainland of Asia. This subregion was known as Indochina, due to the extensive influences from China and South Asia. Varied multicultural and multiethnic groups affect the mainland, which is also a relatively sparsely populated area of Asia, with low levels of urbanization.[28]

Yangon, Myanmar view of Shwedagon Pagoda at dusk.

© ESB Professional/Shutterstock.com

Myanmar[29] (also known[30] as **Burma**)[31] is a protruded state that lies between India on the west and Thailand on the east. The Irrawaddy River flows through the middle of the country and provides a rice-rich lowland basin in the southern part. It is one of the world's poorest economies and was recently controlled by a repressive and abusive[32] military junta, who changed the country's name from Burma. Elections in 2011 began the creation of a parliamentary political system that improved the political climate particularly in the field of media and by releasing of a large number of political prisoners. Politically

Inle Lake Intha fishermen at sunset in Myanmar (Burma).

© R.M. Nunes/Shutterstock.com

and socially, Myanmar has been the most isolated and least westernized of all the countries in Southeast Asia.[34] Calls for boycotts of the country had been common in the past because money spent there supported the military, which most observers and foreign governments deemed brutal in its use of villagers as forced labor and lacking in human rights.[35]

Thailand is a protruded state,[36] and was known as **Siam**. Its capital, Bangkok, is the largest urban center in the mainland subregion. Thailand occupies a central position in the mainland subregion and recently experienced much economic progress.

An indicator of its relatively higher level of development is one of the slowest rates of population growth in all of Southeast Asia.[37] Sadly, it is recognized as one of the top ten countries in the world for human trafficking, with neighboring country Cambodia and several South Asian countries quite active, as well.

Pa-pong-peang rice terrace in north Thailand.

© saravutpics/Shutterstock.com

The Tai people migrated from Southwest China and formed the basis of the language group that today is spoken on much of[38] the mainland subregion. Thailand's population is over 69 million, with about 75 percent Thai.[39] Thailand is a constitutional monarchy and democracy with a king that is seen as a figurehead in the country.

Medical tourism is a growing segment of Thailand's economy (and also popular in Singapore, Malaysia, and India.) Medical tourists tend either to come from highly developed countries (where medical care is very expensive) or from developing countries (where the more wealthy have difficulty finding high-quality medical care). Both medical tourism and leisure tourism have been affected by the country's periodic political instability that significantly divides the rural and urban.[40]

Laos is[41] the only[42] landlocked state with a relatively small population[43] and is among the poorest.[44] Its economic infrastructure is poorly developed, and most of the land, being mountainous, is not suitable for agriculture.[45] It is located

Village and bungalows along Nam Song River in Vang Vieng, Laos.

© Guitar photographer/Shutterstock.com

between the Mekong River, separating it from Thailand to the west and the Annamite Mountain Range, which separates it from Vietnam to the east. About half of its population is ethnic Lao, who live in the lower valleys, while the other half is a mix of hill tribes that live in isolated and remote mountainous areas. These hill tribes make Laos one of the most ethnically diverse countries in Asia, with about 100 different language dialects spoken.[46] Laos is primarily a Communist state and is increasingly pulled into the Chinese sphere of influence.[47]

Cambodia is one of the smallest and poorest countries in Southeast Asia.[48] It is a compact state that is overwhelmingly Khmer in ethnicity. When the U.S. was forced to withdraw from Southeast Asia in 1975, a radical group of young Communists, the Khmer Rouge, undertook a campaign of ethnic cleansing. As many as two million Cambodians were eliminated in what became known as the **killing fields.**[49] Today it is a constitutional monarchy, with a strong one-party rule. The country has had the unfortunate designation of being one of the most popular child prostitution destinations in Asia.[50]

Vietnam, with a population of over 97 million people, has the largest population[51] in mainland region of Southeast Asia,[52] with 87 percent being Vietnamese. Vietnam, Laos, and Cambodia were part of French Indochina. After World War II, Communist forces from China advanced southward into Southeast Asia, especially northern Vietnam. At the time, France still controlled southern Vietnam. War broke out between the French and the Communists. The 1954 Geneva Agreement partitioned the country into a Communist-dominated North and non-Communist South. In the mid-1960s, the U.S. intervened in South Vietnam, Cambodia, and Laos to try to stop the whole area from turning Communist. The basis for American involvement was

Wat Preah Prom Rath beautiful temple in Siem Reap, Cambodia.

© Pelikh Alexey/Shutterstock.com

Vietnam farmer bearing seedlings of rice to plant, in paddy field.

© TOM...foto/Shutterstock.com

the **domino theory,**[53] which says that events that occur in one country will typically cause events of similar nature in neighboring countries. By the mid-1970s, the U.S. withdrew, and eventually Vietnam was reunited into a single country, with Hanoi, the former Communist capital, as the capital of reunited Vietnam. Vietnam now has an emerging economy with increasing trade ties to the West, including the U.S.[54]

Insular

Insular Southeast Asia is a physically fragmented area. Like the mainland subregion, this is a multicultural and multiethnic territory.[55] Historically, these islands were known as the East Indies and the Spice Islands. They have extremely active seismic systems that produce rich agricultural lands and lush, green landscapes in volcanic areas, in addition to large earthquake. Insular Southeast Asia sits directly astride the equator and receives year-round rainfall from the **Intertropical Convergence Zone** (ITCZ.) The ITCZ is an area where air from the north and south collides and rises into the upper atmosphere, forming clouds and rain. Like other areas of Asia, all of Southeast Asia has a monsoonal climate pattern.[56] Insular Southeast Asia includes the countries of[57] Brunei, East Timor, Malaysia, Singapore, Indonesia, and The Philippines.[58]

Brunei is one of three countries that share the island of Borneo,[59] sitting on the north-west edge. It is an oil-exporting Islamic sultanate that intentionally did not achieve independence from the UK until 1984. When Malaysia gained its independence from Britain in 1963, Brunei decided to remain a protectorate under British control. It is one of the world's smallest countries, and one of the largest oil producers east of the Middle East. Because of its vast oil deposits, Brunei's ruling sultan is one of the wealthiest men in the world.[60]

The Sultan Omar Ali Saifuddin Mosque in Bandar Seri Begawan - Brunei

© Ihor Pasternak/Shutterstock.com

East Timor, also known as Timor Leste, comprises the eastern half of the island of Timor, the western half of which is part of Indonesia. When Portugal withdrew from Timor Leste in 1975, the Indonesian government forcibly took control of the former colony, an illegal action not recognized by the United Nations nor the international community. Following a bloody civil war, East Timor gained its independence from Indonesia in 2002. In 2004, Timor Leste had the lowest per capita GDP in the world, about $500 U.S. Living conditions for the over 1.3 million citizens have been difficult as it has attempted to recover (with considerable Australian aid) from the ravages of war. Political instability plagued the new nation, and today there are widespread worries of government corruption, violence, and other criminal activity, all of which slowed economic development in this fragile country.[61] The country continues to grow, with one of the top ten highest natural increase rates in the world and a population growth rate of 2.36 percent.

People at the market at the village of Aituto in the south of East Timor

© amnat30/Shutterstock.com

Malaysia is a fragmented state, with West Malaysia's occupying the southern part of the mainland Malay Peninsula, and East Malaysia's occupying the northwest part of the island of Borneo.[62] Malaysia gained its independence from the UK in 1963, bringing together the British colonies on the Malay Peninsula (Malaya and Singapore) and the two British colonies on Borneo. Ethnic tensions between the Malays and Chinese were a major source of friction within Malaysia, resulting in the island of Singapore's becoming a separate country from Malaysia in 1965. Today,[63] most of the population and area are on the Malay Peninsula, including the capital of Kuala Lumpor. The majority of the populace is ethnically Malay,[64] but large numbers of ethnic Chinese live in Malaysia because of its importance along the trade route between India and China. They were also brought to Malaysia by the British to work on the rubber and palm oil plantations. Malaysia is[65] a world leader in the production of natural rubber, palm oil, and tin.[66]

Kuala Lumpur skyline at dusk Malaysia.
© Patrick Foto/Shutterstock.com

Singapore is[67] an island[68] city-state with a modern infrastructure, no squatter settlements, and a high level of economic development.[69] It sits at the southern end of mainland Malaysia. Singapore is one of the four Asian Tigers that rapidly grew from a less developed to a more developed economy. The country consists of a main island just south of the Malay Peninsula. Given its relative location, Singapore has become one of the busiest ports and container terminals in the world. It is a classic example of an **entrepot**, a place that lies at the intersection of a number of trade paths, making it a major transshipment location. Goods are brought into Singapore, stored, and reshipped to other places, making it a gateway to and from Southeast Asia. The top priority of Singapore's government is to create and improve economic development. The government highly encourages foreign investment by multinational firms from the U.S., Europe, and Japan.[70] Singapore is one of the wealthiest countries in the world and enjoys a high standard of living. The country consistently ranks as one of the least corrupt governments in the world, although it is often criticized for its lack of press and political freedom.[71]

Indonesia is a fragmented state of more than[72] 8,000 islands (6,000 of which are inhabited),[73] many of which are volcanic. Indonesia is the most populated country in the region and is the world's fourth largest country in population. It is

Walkway at the Supertree Grove at Gardens by the Bay in Singapore
© S-F/Shutterstock.com

also the world's most populated Muslim country. The dominant island is Java, the country's core, with nearly 150 million people, and[74] housing the capital city of Jakarta. Java is one of the most densely populated areas of the world,[75] and the Javanese people comprise 42 percent of the total population in the country. More than 300 distinct ethnic groups and more than 250 different languages are spoken across the islands. As a lingua franca that could be understood by inhabitants of the Indonesian archipelago, the Indonesian language was[76] developed in the 1920s and became the country's official language after World war II.

Indonesia's economy is based primarily on tropical agriculture, including coffee, palm oil, tea, tobacco, and tapioca. Indonesia claimed independence from Dutch colonial rule in 1945, although the Dutch did not relinquish full control until 1949.[77]

The Philippines is a fragmented state of more than 7,000 islands. It was a Spanish colony for centuries.[78] Under Spanish rule, land was used to reward those who supported the Spanish. The result was an elite class that controlled the best land in the country, while the impoverished peasants had the worst land or non at all. Land reform is still the number one political issue in the Philippines.[79]

As a result of the Spanish-American War, The Philippines became an American colony and an independent country in 1946. It is only[80] one of two predominantly Christian countries in[81] all of Asia, with Roman Catholicism the main Christian faith. The Philippines has mostly an agricultural economy. Islam is practiced in many of the southern islands, and religion has been the basis for much internal conflict in the southern Philippines.[82] Muslim separatists on the southern island of Mindanao have attempted to break off from the Catholic Philippines since the country's independence and resorted to terror tactics and kidnappings over the years.

The Philippines has attempted a long history of close relations with the US military and, like Thailand, has a reputation for sex tourism that was at least partially related to the foreign military presence. This declined, though it did not completely disappear, after the withdrawal of the last US troops in 1992.

The largest ethnic group is Cebuano (around the island of Cebu), comprising 24 percent of the country's population. Tagalog is the national

Mount Bromo, is an active volcano and part of the Tengger massif, in East Java, Indonesia.

© Kanjanee Chaisin/Shutterstock.com

Sugba Lagoon, Siargao Island, Philippines.

© Mahara/Shutterstock.com

language, although the Tagalog ethnic group makes up only 14 percent of the population. More than 90 different Malay languages are spoken in the Philippines, though at least 50 percent of the population uses English as their lingua franca, due to the legacy of a half century of American rule (1898–1946.)[83]

Review Terms

Burma
compact state
domino theory
elongated state
entrepot
fragmented state

Indochina
Intertropical Convergence
    Zone (ITCZ)
killing fields
medical tourism
perforated state

protruded state
shatter belt
Siam
Southeast Asia
Wallace Line

Research Topics

AFTA
animism
ASEAN
buffer zone
Bumiputra
emerging market
Marxism
Nine-Dash Line
outsourcing
overseas Chinese
pollution exporting
typhoon

Credits

1. **Source:** From Thomas J. Karwoski, *World Regional Geography: An Introduction*, 1st ed., Copyright © 2016 by Kendall Hunt Publishing Company. Reprinted by permission.
2. **Source:** From Thomas J. Karwoski, *World Regional Geography: An Introduction*, 1st ed., Copyright © 2016 by Kendall Hunt Publishing Company. Reprinted by permission.
3. **Source:** From Alan A. Lew, C. Michael Hall, and Dallen J. Timothy, *World Regional Geography: Human Mobilities, Tourism, Destinations, Sustainable Environments*, 2nd ed., Copyright © 2015 by Kendall Hunt Publishing Company. Reprinted by permission.
4. **Source:** From Alan A. Lew, C. Michael Hall, and Dallen J. Timothy, *World Regional Geography: Human Mobilities, Tourism, Destinations, Sustainable Environments*, 2nd ed., Copyright © 2015 by Kendall Hunt Publishing Company. Reprinted by permission.
5. **Source:** From Alan A. Lew, C. Michael Hall, and Dallen J. Timothy, *World Regional Geography: Human Mobilities, Tourism, Destinations, Sustainable Environments*, 2nd ed., Copyright © 2015 by Kendall Hunt Publishing Company. Reprinted by permission.
6. **Source:** From Thomas J. Karwoski, *World Regional Geography: An Introduction*, 1st ed., Copyright © 2016 by Kendall Hunt Publishing Company. Reprinted by permission.

7. **Source:** From Thomas J. Karwoski, *World Regional Geography: An Introduction*, 1st ed., Copyright © 2016 by Kendall Hunt Publishing Company. Reprinted by permission.

8. **Source:** From Alan A. Lew, C. Michael Hall, and Dallen J. Timothy, *World Regional Geography: Human Mobilities, Tourism, Destinations, Sustainable Environments*, 2nd ed., Copyright © 2015 by Kendall Hunt Publishing Company. Reprinted by permission.

9. **Source:** From Alan A. Lew, C. Michael Hall, and Dallen J. Timothy, *World Regional Geography: Human Mobilities, Tourism, Destinations, Sustainable Environments*, 2nd ed., Copyright © 2015 by Kendall Hunt Publishing Company. Reprinted by permission.

10. **Source:** From Alan A. Lew, C. Michael Hall, and Dallen J. Timothy, *World Regional Geography: Human Mobilities, Tourism, Destinations, Sustainable Environments*, 2nd ed., Copyright © 2015 by Kendall Hunt Publishing Company. Reprinted by permission.

11. **Source:** From Alan A. Lew, C. Michael Hall, and Dallen J. Timothy, *World Regional Geography: Human Mobilities, Tourism, Destinations, Sustainable Environments*, 2nd ed., Copyright © 2015 by Kendall Hunt Publishing Company. Reprinted by permission.

12. **Source:** From Thomas J. Karwoski, *World Regional Geography: An Introduction*, 1st ed., Copyright © 2016 by Kendall Hunt Publishing Company. Reprinted by permission.

13. **Source:** From Alan A. Lew, C. Michael Hall, and Dallen J. Timothy, *World Regional Geography: Human Mobilities, Tourism, Destinations, Sustainable Environments*, 2nd ed., Copyright © 2015 by Kendall Hunt Publishing Company. Reprinted by permission.

14. **Source:** From Thomas J. Karwoski, *World Regional Geography: An Introduction*, 1st ed., Copyright © 2016 by Kendall Hunt Publishing Company. Reprinted by permission.

15. **Source:** From Thomas J. Karwoski, *World Regional Geography: An Introduction*, 1st ed., Copyright © 2016 by Kendall Hunt Publishing Company. Reprinted by permission.

16. **Source:** From Alan A. Lew, C. Michael Hall, and Dallen J. Timothy, *World Regional Geography: Human Mobilities, Tourism, Destinations, Sustainable Environments*, 2nd ed., Copyright © 2015 by Kendall Hunt Publishing Company. Reprinted by permission.

17. **Source:** From Thomas J. Karwoski, *World Regional Geography: An Introduction*, 1st ed., Copyright © 2016 by Kendall Hunt Publishing Company. Reprinted by permission.

18. **Source:** From Alan A. Lew, C. Michael Hall, and Dallen J. Timothy, *World Regional Geography: Human Mobilities, Tourism, Destinations, Sustainable Environments*, 2nd ed., Copyright © 2015 by Kendall Hunt Publishing Company. Reprinted by permission.

19. **Source:** From Alan A. Lew, C. Michael Hall, and Dallen J. Timothy, *World Regional Geography: Human Mobilities, Tourism, Destinations, Sustainable Environments*, 2nd ed., Copyright © 2015 by Kendall Hunt Publishing Company. Reprinted by permission.

20. **Source:** From Alan A. Lew, C. Michael Hall, and Dallen J. Timothy, *World Regional Geography: Human Mobilities, Tourism, Destinations, Sustainable Environments*, 2nd ed., Copyright © 2015 by Kendall Hunt Publishing Company. Reprinted by permission.

21. **Source:** From Alan A. Lew, C. Michael Hall, and Dallen J. Timothy, *World Regional Geography: Human Mobilities, Tourism, Destinations, Sustainable Environments*, 2nd ed., Copyright © 2015 by Kendall Hunt Publishing Company. Reprinted by permission.

22. **Source:** From Thomas J. Karwoski, *World Regional Geography: An Introduction*, 1st ed., Copyright © 2016 by Kendall Hunt Publishing Company. Reprinted by permission.

23. **Source:** From Thomas J. Karwoski, *World Regional Geography: An Introduction*, 1st ed., Copyright © 2016 by Kendall Hunt Publishing Company. Reprinted by permission.

24. **Source:** From Thomas J. Karwoski, *World Regional Geography: An Introduction*, 1st ed., Copyright © 2016 by Kendall Hunt Publishing Company. Reprinted by permission.

25. **Source:** From Thomas J. Karwoski, *World Regional Geography: An Introduction*, 1st ed., Copyright © 2016 by Kendall Hunt Publishing Company. Reprinted by permission.

26. **Source:** From Thomas J. Karwoski, *World Regional Geography: An Introduction*, 1st ed., Copyright © 2016 by Kendall Hunt Publishing Company. Reprinted by permission.

27. **Source:** From Thomas J. Karwoski, *World Regional Geography: An Introduction*, 1st ed., Copyright © 2016 by Kendall Hunt Publishing Company. Reprinted by permission.

28. **Source:** From Thomas J. Karwoski, *World Regional Geography: An Introduction*, 1st ed., Copyright © 2016 by Kendall Hunt Publishing Company. Reprinted by permission.

29. **Source:** From Thomas J. Karwoski, *World Regional Geography: An Introduction*, 1st ed., Copyright © 2016 by Kendall Hunt Publishing Company. Reprinted by permission.

30. **Source:** From Alan A. Lew, C. Michael Hall, and Dallen J. Timothy, *World Regional Geography: Human Mobilities, Tourism, Destinations, Sustainable Environments*, 2nd ed., Copyright © 2015 by Kendall Hunt Publishing Company. Reprinted by permission.

31. **Source:** From Alan A. Lew, C. Michael Hall, and Dallen J. Timothy, *World Regional Geography: Human Mobilities, Tourism, Destinations, Sustainable Environments*, 2nd ed., Copyright © 2015 by Kendall Hunt Publishing Company. Reprinted by permission.

32. **Source:** From Thomas J. Karwoski, *World Regional Geography: An Introduction*, 1st ed., Copyright © 2016 by Kendall Hunt Publishing Company. Reprinted by permission.

33. **Source:** From Alan A. Lew, C. Michael Hall, and Dallen J. Timothy, *World Regional Geography: Human Mobilities, Tourism, Destinations, Sustainable Environments*, 2nd ed., Copyright © 2015 by Kendall Hunt Publishing Company. Reprinted by permission.

34. **Source:** From Thomas J. Karwoski, *World Regional Geography: An Introduction*, 1st ed., Copyright © 2016 by Kendall Hunt Publishing Company. Reprinted by permission.

35. **Source:** From Alan A. Lew, C. Michael Hall, and Dallen J. Timothy, *World Regional Geography: Human Mobilities, Tourism, Destinations, Sustainable Environments*, 2nd ed., Copyright © 2015 by Kendall Hunt Publishing Company. Reprinted by permission.

36. **Source:** From Thomas J. Karwoski, *World Regional Geography: An Introduction*, 1st ed., Copyright © 2016 by Kendall Hunt Publishing Company. Reprinted by permission.

37. **Source:** From Thomas J. Karwoski, *World Regional Geography: An Introduction*, 1st ed., Copyright © 2016 by Kendall Hunt Publishing Company. Reprinted by permission.

38. **Source:** From Alan A. Lew, C. Michael Hall, and Dallen J. Timothy, *World Regional Geography: Human Mobilities, Tourism, Destinations, Sustainable Environments*, 2nd ed., Copyright © 2015 by Kendall Hunt Publishing Company. Reprinted by permission.

39. **Source:** From Alan A. Lew, C. Michael Hall, and Dallen J. Timothy, *World Regional Geography: Human Mobilities, Tourism, Destinations, Sustainable Environments*, 2nd ed., Copyright © 2015 by Kendall Hunt Publishing Company. Reprinted by permission.

40. **Source:** From Alan A. Lew, C. Michael Hall, and Dallen J. Timothy, *World Regional Geography: Human Mobilities, Tourism, Destinations, Sustainable Environments*, 2nd ed., Copyright © 2015 by Kendall Hunt Publishing Company. Reprinted by permission.

41. **Source:** From Thomas J. Karwoski, *World Regional Geography: An Introduction*, 1st ed., Copyright © 2016 by Kendall Hunt Publishing Company. Reprinted by permission.

42. **Source:** From Alan A. Lew, C. Michael Hall, and Dallen J. Timothy, *World Regional Geography: Human Mobilities, Tourism, Destinations, Sustainable Environments*, 2nd ed., Copyright © 2015 by Kendall Hunt Publishing Company. Reprinted by permission.

43. **Source:** From Thomas J. Karwoski, *World Regional Geography: An Introduction*, 1st ed., Copyright © 2016 by Kendall Hunt Publishing Company. Reprinted by permission.

44. From Alan A. Lew, C. Michael Hall, and Dallen J. Timothy, *World Regional Geography: Human Mobilities, Tourism, Destinations, Sustainable Environments*, 2nd ed., Copyright © 2015 by Kendall Hunt Publishing Company. Reprinted by permission.

45. **Source:** From Thomas J. Karwoski, *World Regional Geography: An Introduction*, 1st ed., Copyright © 2016 by Kendall Hunt Publishing Company. Reprinted by permission.

46. **Source:** From Alan A. Lew, C. Michael Hall, and Dallen J. Timothy, *World Regional Geography: Human Mobilities, Tourism, Destinations, Sustainable Environments*, 2nd ed., Copyright © 2015 by Kendall Hunt Publishing Company. Reprinted by permission.

47. **Source:** From Thomas J. Karwoski, *World Regional Geography: An Introduction*, 1st ed., Copyright © 2016 by Kendall Hunt Publishing Company. Reprinted by permission.

48. **Source:** From Alan A. Lew, C. Michael Hall, and Dallen J. Timothy, *World Regional Geography: Human Mobilities, Tourism, Destinations, Sustainable Environments*, 2nd ed., Copyright © 2015 by Kendall Hunt Publishing Company. Reprinted by permission.

49. **Source:** From Thomas J. Karwoski, *World Regional Geography: An Introduction*, 1st ed., Copyright © 2016 by Kendall Hunt Publishing Company. Reprinted by permission.

50. **Source:** From Alan A. Lew, C. Michael Hall, and Dallen J. Timothy, *World Regional Geography: Human Mobilities, Tourism, Destinations, Sustainable Environments*, 2nd ed., Copyright © 2015 by Kendall Hunt Publishing Company. Reprinted by permission.

51. **Source:** From Alan A. Lew, C. Michael Hall, and Dallen J. Timothy, *World Regional Geography: Human Mobilities, Tourism, Destinations, Sustainable Environments*, 2nd ed., Copyright © 2015 by Kendall Hunt Publishing Company. Reprinted by permission.

52. **Source:** From Alan A. Lew, C. Michael Hall, and Dallen J. Timothy, *World Regional Geography: Human Mobilities, Tourism, Destinations, Sustainable Environments*, 2nd ed., Copyright © 2015 by Kendall Hunt Publishing Company. Reprinted by permission.

53. **Source:** From Thomas J. Karwoski, *World Regional Geography: An Introduction*, 1st ed., Copyright © 2016 by Kendall Hunt Publishing Company. Reprinted by permission.

54. **Source:** From Thomas J. Karwoski, *World Regional Geography: An Introduction*, 1st ed., Copyright © 2016 by Kendall Hunt Publishing Company. Reprinted by permission.

55. **Source:** From Thomas J. Karwoski, *World Regional Geography: An Introduction*, 1st ed., Copyright © 2016 by Kendall Hunt Publishing Company. Reprinted by permission.

56. **Source:** From Alan A. Lew, C. Michael Hall, and Dallen J. Timothy, *World Regional Geography: Human Mobilities, Tourism, Destinations, Sustainable Environments*, 2nd ed., Copyright © 2015 by Kendall Hunt Publishing Company. Reprinted by permission.

57. **Source:** From Thomas J. Karwoski, *World Regional Geography: An Introduction*, 1st ed., Copyright © 2016 by Kendall Hunt Publishing Company. Reprinted by permission.

58. **Source:** From Thomas J. Karwoski, *World Regional Geography: An Introduction*, 1st ed., Copyright © 2016 by Kendall Hunt Publishing Company. Reprinted by permission.

59. **Source:** From Alan A. Lew, C. Michael Hall, and Dallen J. Timothy, *World Regional Geography: Human Mobilities, Tourism, Destinations, Sustainable Environments*, 2nd ed., Copyright © 2015 by Kendall Hunt Publishing Company. Reprinted by permission.

60. **Source:** From Alan A. Lew, C. Michael Hall, and Dallen J. Timothy, *World Regional Geography: Human Mobilities, Tourism, Destinations, Sustainable Environments*, 2nd ed., Copyright © 2015 by Kendall Hunt Publishing Company. Reprinted by permission.

61. **Source:** From Alan A. Lew, C. Michael Hall, and Dallen J. Timothy, *World Regional Geography: Human Mobilities, Tourism, Destinations, Sustainable Environments*, 2nd ed., Copyright © 2015 by Kendall Hunt Publishing Company. Reprinted by permission.

62. **Source:** From Thomas J. Karwoski, *World Regional Geography: An Introduction*, 1st ed., Copyright © 2016 by Kendall Hunt Publishing Company. Reprinted by permission.

63. **Source:** From Alan A. Lew, C. Michael Hall, and Dallen J. Timothy, *World Regional Geography: Human Mobilities, Tourism, Destinations, Sustainable Environments*, 2nd ed., Copyright © 2015 by Kendall Hunt Publishing Company. Reprinted by permission.

64. **Source:** From Thomas J. Karwoski, *World Regional Geography: An Introduction*, 1st ed., Copyright © 2016 by Kendall Hunt Publishing Company. Reprinted by permission.

65. From Alan A. Lew, C. Michael Hall, and Dallen J. Timothy, *World Regional Geography: Human Mobilities, Tourism, Destinations, Sustainable Environments*, 2nd ed., Copyright © 2015 by Kendall Hunt Publishing Company. Reprinted by permission.

66. From Alan A. Lew, C. Michael Hall, and Dallen J. Timothy, *World Regional Geography: Human Mobilities, Tourism, Destinations, Sustainable Environments*, 2nd ed., Copyright © 2015 by Kendall Hunt Publishing Company. Reprinted by permission.

67. **Source:** From Thomas J. Karwoski, *World Regional Geography: An Introduction*, 1st ed., Copyright © 2016 by Kendall Hunt Publishing Company. Reprinted by permission.

68. **Source:** From Alan A. Lew, C. Michael Hall, and Dallen J. Timothy, *World Regional Geography: Human Mobilities, Tourism, Destinations, Sustainable Environments*, 2nd ed., Copyright © 2015 by Kendall Hunt Publishing Company. Reprinted by permission.

69. **Source:** From Thomas J. Karwoski, *World Regional Geography: An Introduction*, 1st ed., Copyright © 2016 by Kendall Hunt Publishing Company. Reprinted by permission.

70. **Source:** From Thomas J. Karwoski, *World Regional Geography: An Introduction*, 1st ed., Copyright © 2016 by Kendall Hunt Publishing Company. Reprinted by permission.

71. **Source:** From Alan A. Lew, C. Michael Hall, and Dallen J. Timothy, *World Regional Geography: Human Mobilities, Tourism, Destinations, Sustainable Environments*, 2nd ed., Copyright © 2015 by Kendall Hunt Publishing Company. Reprinted by permission.

72. **Source:** From Thomas J. Karwoski, *World Regional Geography: An Introduction*, 1st ed., Copyright © 2016 by Kendall Hunt Publishing Company. Reprinted by permission.

73. **Source:** From Alan A. Lew, C. Michael Hall, and Dallen J. Timothy, *World Regional Geography: Human Mobilities, Tourism, Destinations, Sustainable Environments*, 2nd ed., Copyright © 2015 by Kendall Hunt Publishing Company. Reprinted by permission.

74. **Source:** From Thomas J. Karwoski, *World Regional Geography: An Introduction*, 1st ed., Copyright © 2016 by Kendall Hunt Publishing Company. Reprinted by permission.

75. **Source:** From Thomas J. Karwoski, *World Regional Geography: An Introduction*, 1st ed., Copyright © 2016 by Kendall Hunt Publishing Company. Reprinted by permission.

76. **Source:** From Alan A. Lew, C. Michael Hall, and Dallen J. Timothy, *World Regional Geography: Human Mobilities, Tourism, Destinations, Sustainable Environments*, 2nd ed., Copyright © 2015 by Kendall Hunt Publishing Company. Reprinted by permission.

77. **Source:** From Alan A. Lew, C. Michael Hall, and Dallen J. Timothy, *World Regional Geography: Human Mobilities, Tourism, Destinations, Sustainable Environments*, 2nd ed., Copyright © 2015 by Kendall Hunt Publishing Company. Reprinted by permission.

78. **Source:** From Thomas J. Karwoski, *World Regional Geography: An Introduction*, 1st ed., Copyright © 2016 by Kendall Hunt Publishing Company. Reprinted by permission.

79. **Source:** From Alan A. Lew, C. Michael Hall, and Dallen J. Timothy, *World Regional Geography: Human Mobilities, Tourism, Destinations, Sustainable Environments*, 2nd ed., Copyright © 2015 by Kendall Hunt Publishing Company. Reprinted by permission.

80. **Source:** From Thomas J. Karwoski, *World Regional Geography: An Introduction*, 1st ed., Copyright © 2016 by Kendall Hunt Publishing Company. Reprinted by permission.

81. **Source:** From Thomas J. Karwoski, *World Regional Geography: An Introduction*, 1st ed., Copyright © 2016 by Kendall Hunt Publishing Company. Reprinted by permission.

82. **Source:** From Thomas J. Karwoski, *World Regional Geography: An Introduction*, 1st ed., Copyright © 2016 by Kendall Hunt Publishing Company. Reprinted by permission.

83. **Source:** From Alan A. Lew, C. Michael Hall, and Dallen J. Timothy, *World Regional Geography: Human Mobilities, Tourism, Destinations, Sustainable Environments*, 2nd ed., Copyright © 2015 by Kendall Hunt Publishing Company. Reprinted by permission.

Chapter 10

NORTH AFRICA AND SOUTHWEST ASIA

The global importance of the Middle East is that it keeps the Far East and the Near East from encroaching on each other.

—Dan Quayle

Where are North Africa and Southwest Asia?

The regions of **North Africa** and **Southwest Asia** include the Mediterranean coast of North Africa across the Sahara Desert to the countries of Southeast Asia, which include subregions of the Middle East, the Arabian Peninsula, and Empire States. North Africa and Southwest Asia sit in the Northern Hemisphere, and this region sits on two continents in the Northern and Eastern Hemispheres. It resides on the African tectonic plate and the southwestern edge of the Eurasian tectonic plate and is influenced by the minor tectonic plates: Arabian and Somalian.

The North Africa and Southwest Asian Region.

© Peter Hermes Furian/Shutterstock.com

Why are North Africa and Southwest Asia in the same region?

Several commonalities link this vast global area. Dry climate conditions with low amounts of precipitation are common in most of the region. The Afro-Asiatic language family is used in North Africa and much of the Middle East and Arabian Peninsula. Islam is the primary religion in most of the region. Dry climates mean most of the region is relatively

125

less populated than Sub-Saharan Africa, and many important cultural developments originated here.

Major Qualities of North Africa and Southwest Asia

Spatially, this region is at a world crossroads, interconnecting Europe, Africa, and Asia. Physically, dry or arid climate conditions dominate this area. It includes the world's largest known deposits and reserves of oil. All three of the world's western and monotheistic religions originated here and spread to other places. Many early culture hearths developed around Mesopotamia and the Nile River Valley. Demographically, population is concentrated in discontinuous clusters around infrequent water sources. Today, there is continued cultural and political conflict that affects peoples and states within the region.[4]

Moroccan ruins in Atlas Mountains, Morocco, Africa

© Mikadun/Shutterstock.com

Geologically, Southwest Asia is a region of considerable tectonic activity. The African and Eurasian continents collide here, creating alpine orogeny mountain systems, including the Atlas Mountains in North Africa, Asia Minor and the Caucasus Mountains, the Zagros Mountains of Iran and the Hindu Kush Range, which branches out from the Pamir Knot.[5]

Near, Middle and Far East

The term **Middle East** was first used to define Southwest Asia by the British India Office in the 1850s. It referred to the region east of the Ottoman Empire (today's Turkey was the **Near East**) and centered on the Persian Gulf. This definition, however, was widely criticized for its geographical inaccuracy and later for its Eurocentrism. Until WWII, confusion continued over the use of Near East and Middle East, though it was well established that China and Southeast

The Middle East oil accounts for 40% of the world's known oil.

© Bruce Rolff/Shutterstock.com

Asia were the **Far East**. After World War II, the term Near East was dropped from popular use and Middle East has come into common acceptance. Despite its wide acceptance by new media organizations, the term Middle East is still not clearly defined.[6]

Environmental Adaptation

In the hot dry desert area, buildings in towns and cities are traditionally built close together to protect against heat and wind. Although winds from the upper atmosphere are generally not strong, the daytime heat rising from the desert landscape can create strong convection winds. Making a building compact is like raising the ground level, with the affecting the roofs of the houses, while the interior spaces below remain cooler, like a cave in a mountainside. Courtyards provide shade and an opportunity for circulation of air as winds pass overhead and pull cooler air from below. Round roofs, common features of the region's traditional architecture, also contribute to this circulation of air. Some traditional buildings use wind towers, which are about 45 to 140 feet high and collect air at their top on their windward side (facing into the wind), directing it into the house and then exhausting the wind through the windows on the leeward (back) side of the building. Water channels, wells and water fountains are also used in traditional architecture to keep the indoors cool as the air passes through.[8]

Morocco, Ouarzazate - Ait Ben Haddou Medieval Kasbah, built in adobe - UNESCO World Heritage Site. Location for many films - Gladiator, Babel, Alexander, Game of Thrones and The Mummy

© John Copland/Shutterstock.com

Oil

The sand-covered flat lands of Southwest Asia and North Africa are estimated to contain two-thirds of the world's oil reserves, and they are of strategic global geopolitical importance. The modern economies of some areas, especially on the Arabian Peninsula, have been transformed by the region's oil and gas wealth. Although some oil fields were initially drilled by British and American oil companies in the first half of the 20th century, it was the development of oil by companies owned by the countries in the region in the 1960s and 1970s that provided both the basis for rapid economic expansion in the region and changes in the world's geopolitical balance. While the oil economy has provided the basis for the development of petrochemical industries, the countries of the region have been diversifying their economic base. In addition, a number of Gulf countries, such as the United Arab Emirates and Qatar, have developed substantial airlines and airline infrastructure in an attempt to position themselves as global transport, business, tourism, and leisure hubs.[7]

Sea Sands and Arid Climate Zones

These flat land areas are covered by the large sand seas of the Sahara Desert and the Arabian Desert. Sahara is translated as Great Desert, so some pepole prefer to just use the word by itself, while others prefer the traditional full name. Together, these two seas of sand extend 5,000 miles from east to west. They were formed by erosion of the underlying rock by wind, water and time. The area has very little cloud

The Sahara and Arabian Deserts.

© Cromagnon/Shutterstock.com

cover, causing extremes of daytime heat and nighttime cold. The Rub' al Khali (Empty Quarter) of the Arabian Desert covers much of the Arabian Peninsula and is the largest true desert in the world. A true desert of a solid expanse of sand seas with no vegetation. The entire region, extending across North Africa and into Asia, has a hot, dry climate.[9]

The largest expanse of dry, arid and desert lands on the planet extends from the Atlantic Ocean to the Indian Ocean and into Central Asia. The reason for this vast arid climate zone is the location of the African continent on the surface of the Earth. The main variables in climate are seasonal changes and precipitation, arid climates have little or no rain throughout the year. Drier climates are found just north and south of the tropical equator and are either arid (little rainfall) and generally found on the western sides of continents or subtropical (hot summer; cool winter) and found on the eastern sides of continents. Further north of these regions is another belt of humid climates, including the Mediterranean.[10]

Cultural Hearth

Two main early world civilizations began in North Africa and Southwest Asia. The Nile River Valley was the site of early cultural developments and kingdoms, including the building of the pyramids. The **Nile River** is the longest river in the world, flowing south to north from the

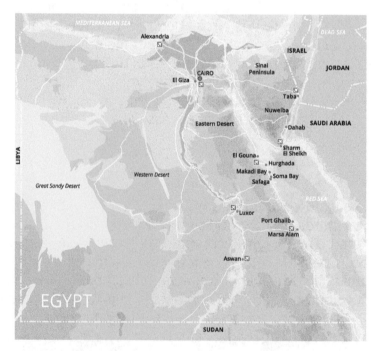

Egypt with capital Cairo, and the River Nile.

© Cromagnon/Shutterstock.com

mountains of eastern Africa to its end at the Mediterranean Sea. In Southwest Asia, the **Fertile Crescent** is an area stretching from the eastern Mediterranean coast to the head of the Persian Gulf. Within the Fertile Crescent, a smaller area between the Tigris and the Euphrates rivers. Is historically known as **Mesopotamia**, where the earliest archaeological evidence of cities and agriculture originated. The modern state of Iraq comprises most of Mesopotamia.[11]

Patterns of Religion

Three major world religions originated in Southwest Asia: Judaism, Christianity, and Islam. These three religions are all considered as western and monotheistic. Judaism is the oldest of the western monotheistic religions, tracing its ancestry to the prophet **Abraham**. It is numerically the smallest of the major world religions, with[12] over 15 million adherents[13] worldwide. Judaism dominates only in one country, Israel. Due to its small size and localized concentration, it is known as an ethnic religion. Judaism Jains one major sacred site, the **Western Wall**, in the old city of Jerusalem. Jews believe this is the only remaining part of a temple largely destroyed by the Romans. Over time, three different philosophical branches of Judaism evolved. The most traditional is the **Orthodox branch;** the most liberal is the **Reformed branch**. The **Conservative branch** is philosophically between the other two branches.

Christianity is a universalizing religion that grew out of the older, ethnic Judaism about 2,000 years ago. **Jesus Christ**, the founder of Christianity, was a Jew. Early on, Christianity spread from the eastern Mediterranean into southern Europe, became associated with European culture, and globally spread with the extensive migrations of Europeans. The three branches of Christianity were discussed in the Europe region chapter.

Islam is the youngest of the western monotheistic religions. It originated in Southwest Asia, in the Arabian Peninsula. Similar to Christianity, Islam is a universalizing religion. The founder of Islam is the prophet **Muhammad** who officially began the new religion in 622 A.D. in the city of Madinah. Islam shares many of the same prophets as Judaism and Christianity, including Abraham, Moses, and Jesus. The main holy book of Islam is the **Quran**.

The essence of Islam is identified by the **Five Pillars of Faith**. The first pillar of faith is the reciting of the basic creed—"there is no God but Allah and Muhammad is his prophet." A second pillar of faith is daily prayer facing (Makkah)[14] Mecca. The third pillar

Muslim pilgrims from all over the world gather to perform a small Umrah or Hajj at the Grand Mosque in Mecca, Saudi Arabia

© BiksuTong/Shutterstock.com

of faith is fasting from sunrise to sunset during the Muslim month of Ramadan. Almsgiving to the poor and needy is the fourth pillar. The fifth pillar is making a "hajj," or a pilgrimage to Makkah during one's life.[15]

There are three major sacred sites for Islam: Mecca, Madinah, and Jerusalem. **Mecca** is the[16] most sacred site. This is the birthplace of the prophet Muhammad. **Medina** is the[17] next most sacred site. It is the city where the religion was founded by Muhammad, and it is where the tomb of the prophet is found. **Jerusalem** is the[18] last of the most sacred sites

Western Wall at the Dome of the Rock on the Temple Mount in Jerusalem, Israel

© VanderWolf Images/Shutterstock.com

for Islam. Above the Jewish Western Wall is the Temple Mount, the historic location of the temple of King Solomon in Jewish history. The Dome of the Rock is found at the Temple Mount, and commemorates the ascent of Muhammad to heaven and back to earth.[20]

Over time, two major branches of Islam emerged. The **Sunni** branch is the majority branch of Islam.[21] Nearly 90 percent of all Muslims in the world are the Sunni Muslims. The **Shiite** branch is the minority branch, dominating only in Iran and Iraq. Sunnis believe in an elected leadership, whereas Shiites believe leadership must be traced directly back to the prophet Muhammad through his son-in-law Ali and grandson Hussein. Philosophically, Sunnis tend to be more moderate and accepting of outside ideas. Shiites tend to be more fundamental and traditional in their beliefs. The Shiites have two sacred sites of their own: Najaf and Karbala, both in Iraq. Najaf is the location of the tomb of Ali; Karbala is the location of the tomb of Hussein.

There are historical, philosophy, and language connections between Jews and Muslims. Historically, both Jews and Muslims trace their ultimate ancestry to the prophet Abraham. Jews are linked to Abraham through his marriage to Sarah and their eventual son Isaac. Muslims are linked to Abraham through his relations with a servant Hagar and their son Ishmael. Philosophically, both Jews and Muslims are monotheists. Linguistically, Jews and Muslims both speak languages, Hebrew and Arabic, which are part of the Afro-Asiatic language family and the Semitic language subfamily.[22]

The North African and Southwest Asian Region

North Africa and Southwest Asia consist of five subregions: the Maghreb[23] and the adjacent states, the Nile River Valley, the Arabian Peninsula, the Middle East, and the Empire States.[24]

The Maghreb and[25] the Adjacent States

The Maghreb refers to the northwest coastal states of Africa (Algeria, Tunisia, and Morocco with Western Sahara), and[26] the adjacent states (Mauritania, Mali, Burkina Faso, Niger, Chad, and Libya) refer to the southern neighboring countries surrounding the Maghreb. The Maghreb coast has more humid conditions than the rest of North Africa and supports a relatively dense concentration of people.

Morocco is located on the northwest coast of Africa, south of Gibraltar. Formerly a French colony, It is a conservative kingdom that includes the cities of Casablanca, Marrakech, and Tangier.[27] Western Sahara is a stateless territory, administered by Morocco.[28] A small portion of its land is disputed and controlled by the Sahrawi Arab Democratic Republic.

Algeria is another former French colony that fought a bitter conflict for liberation in the 1950s and early 1960s. Many Algerians emigrated to France, where they form one of Europe's largest Muslim populations.[29]

Tunisia is the smallest of the Maghreb states. In 2011, Tunisia was the origin of the Arab Spring. The **Arab Spring** was a wave of internal revolt, greatly assisted by the use of social media, against repressive and corrupt governments in the Arab World. The Arab Spring eventually spread to Libya and Egypt and finally to Syria.[30]

Mauritania is a flat country of law population that is predominately desert on the western edge of North Africa. It has Berber roots and limited civil rights and human liberties. Slavery was made illegal only in 2007.

Mali is a landlocked country in the Sahara with numerous natural resources, including gold and salt. It was under France's control in the latter portion of the 1800s and continues official language. Mali is also the home of the ancient city of Timbuktu.

Panorama of the city centre of Algiers, the capital of Algeria

© Leonid Andronov/Shutterstock.com

Desert land of Niamey, Niger.

© mbrand85/Shutterstock.com

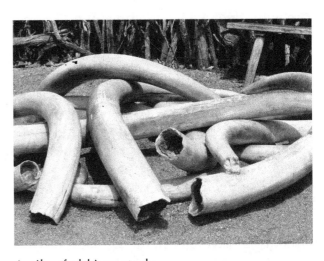

A pile of old ivory tusks

© Svetlana Foote/Shutterstock.com

Burkina Faso is a landlocked country with a history of coups and protests. It is the second largest populated country in the adjacent states of the Maghreb, with over twenty million people. Its economy is tied mainly to gold and cotton. Life (age) expectancy is only in the late 50s, as is common with many of its neighboring countries.

Niger is a landlocked less developed country that won its independence in 1960 but has since had multiple military regimes gain control. The population natural increase rate is quite high in Niger, and nearly half the population is under the age of 18.

The pyramids and the Sphinx, in Cairo, Egypt.

© Merydolla/Shutterstock.com

Chad is mainly a landlocked desert country but sits at the edge of different biomes, including a wetland area around Lake Chad. **Poaching** (illegal hunting or catching) is an issue for the country's large mammal species. Lastly, domino effect conflict has historically impacted Chad from neighboring Sudan, with problems spilling over the border.

Libya[31] is an adjacent state to The Maghreb. It is an important oil producer and exporter. During the Arab Spring of 2011, the dictator Gadhafi was overthrown and killed.[32] Its economy is tied to oil and its lands are dry with areas that may see no rainfall in an entire calender.

The Nile River Valley

The Nile River Valley includes the[33] region around the basin of the Nile River. Egypt is considered to be the heart of the[34] North African region. Its centralized position west to east, its prominence as a historic early world culture hearth, its status as the most populated Arab country, and its influence within Islam all combine to make Egypt the center of the region. The Arab Spring in Egypt led to the overthrow of President Mubarak[35] in 2011.

Egypt also boasts the **Suez Canal** that was opened in 1869 and recently underwent expansion in 2015. The Suez is one of only two outlets for sea faring vessels in the Mediterranean Sea. It allows for an alternative passage to Atlantic Ocean and Indian Ocean connections, where the previous route requried circumnavigation around the southern edge of Africa.

Sudan is a largely desert country, centered on the confluence of the Blue Nile and White Nile[36] rivers, tributaries that flow north into the Nile. Decades of civil war between north and south impoverished the country and eventually led to the political separation of Sudan and South Sudan. A particularly violent part of Sudan's recent history occurred in the western province of **Darfur**. Where hundreds of thousands of people were killed, and several million people were driven from their homes[37] when two rebel groups engaged with the local goverment.

The Arabian Peninsula

The **Arabian Peninsula** lies south of Jordan and Iraq, adjacent to the Red Sea, the Arabian Sea, and the Persian Gulf.

Saudi Arabia occupies most of the land area and has the largest population on the peninsula. Saudi Arabia is the world leader in oil production and has the largest concentration of oil reserves in the world.[38] The country is economically overdependent on oil production, presenting a challenge when the price of the barrel drops. The country includes the two most important sacred places in Islam, Mecca and Medina.

Kuwait is an oil-rich country at the head of the Persian Gulf. Iraq's invasion of Kuwait in the early 1990s led to the First Gulf War.[39] The country is known for a high number of foreign workers and for its heart shape.

Bahrain is an island state ruled by a royal family. It is a major banking center, with a predominantly Shiite population. Nearly two-thirds of its work force is foreign. The U.S. Navy's Fifth Fleet is headquartered here.

Qatar is a peninsula country neighboring Bahrain. It is rich in oil and natural gas. Qatar is home to the media giant Al Jazeera.

The United Arab Emirates (U.A.E), is a federation of various emirates. The two most well-known emirates are Abu Dhabi and Dubai. These two emirates have the area's largest reserves of oil. Dubai includes the Burj Khalifa, the world's tallest building,[40] at 2,717 feet.

Kuwait City at night

© Ibrahim muhamed/Shutterstock.com

Dubai skyline, UAE.

© Luciano Mortula—LGM/Shutterstock.com

The destruction and remnants of war caused by the militias of Houthi and its war on the city of Taiz, South Yemen since early 2015. (October 2018.)

© anasalhajj/Shutterstock.com

Yemen occupies the southwest part of the Arabian Peninsula. A Shiite rebellion against the central government destabilized the north, and a secessionist movement occurs in the south. Al-Qaeda and other terrorist groups are highly concentrated within the country.[41]

Oman is an Islamic Arab country at the southern edge of the Arabian Peninsula. The Sultan (absolute monarch) of Oman is the longest serving leader in the subregion and has held office since 1970. In sharp contrast to Yemen, it is a fairly peaceful country. The Strait of Hormuz is a strategic **choke point** (narrow route that can restrict or control sea travel) for vessels traveling from the Persian Gulf to the Indian Ocean.

The destroyed city of Homs in Syria

© Smallcreative/Shutterstock.com

The Middle East

Five countries comprise the Middle East: Iraq, Syria, Jordan, Lebanon, and Israel.

Iraq is the largest state in population and area within the subregion. Iraq is a multinational state, comprised of three main ethnic groups: Shiites, Sunnis, and Kurds. The Shiites are the overall majority group in the south. Under the rule of Saddam Hussein, the majority Shiites faced great discrimination. The Sunnis occupy the central and western areas. They controlled the government under Hussein, who was overthrown in the Second Gulf war. The **Kurds** are a [42] stateless nation in the north[43] and along the borders

The Al Khazneh Temple in the ancient city of Petra, Jordan.

© Aleksandra H. Kossowska/Shutterstock.com

of Iraq and Turkey. Similar to the Shiites, the Kurds were greatly discriminated against under the Hussein administration. The terrorist group **ISIS,** the Islamic State of Iraq and Syria,[44] (ISIL—the Islamic State of Iraq and the Levant) is involved in much of the conflict in Iraq[45] and the surrounding region that is sometimes called the **Levant,** the lands of the eastern Mediterranean Sea.

Syria is a multinational state ruled by an oppressive leader, Bashar al-Assad, and is often considered a **failed state,** due to leadership's not protecting their people. The Arab Spring was unsuccessful in Syria. Syria has tremendous internal instability. Government forces under Assad are supported by Russia; anti- government forces are aided by the U.S.; and ISIS is headquartered in Syria.[46] It is estimated that over 100,000 Syrians have been killed, and nearly 5 million have become refugees in surrounding countries.

Jordan is a moderate-sized poor country, lacking oil resources. The majority of the population is ethnic Palestinian.[47] The ancient city of Petra is prominent in the carved sandstone rocks.

Lebanon is a small country on the eastern Mediterranean coast. Its many religious and ethnic factions cause much political instability. An Iran-sponsored terrorist group, **Hezbollah**, is a major political force in southern Lebanon. Hizbollah has been involved in many anti-Israeli activities and conflicts.[48]

Cedars of Lebanon, beautiful ancient cedar tree forest in the mountains, of Bsharre.

© Anna Om/Shutterstock.com

Israel is a Jewish state, created in 1948. That year, the British pulled out of its Palestine territory. Israel is distinctive in being neither Arab nor Muslim. Soon after proclaiming Israel as a state, Egyptian, Iraqi, Jordanian, and Syrian forces invaded during the 1948 War of Independence. In 1967, the Six-Day War resulted in another Israeli victory, and Israel gained control of the Sinai Peninsula, Gaza Strip, West Bank of the Jordan River, and the Golan Heights on the Syria border. Eventually, the Sinai Peninsula was given back to Egypt. The Golan Heights, Gaza Strip, and West Bank remain as Israeli occupied territories. The Palestinian Arabs, like the Kurds, are another example of a stateless nation in this region. In the Gaza Strip, a radical Palestinian group, Hamas, is dominant.[49]

The Empire States

The **Empire States** consist of two countries, Turkey and Iran,[50] and the island country of Cyprus. Turkey was the historical word for the Ottoman Empire, and Iran was the word for the Persian Empire. They are both demographically significant, as they are the most populated countries in the entrie region. Culturally, the Turks and Iranians do not speak Arabic languages; the Turks speak an Altaic language, and Iran speaks an Indo-European language. Religiously, Iran is Shiite Islam, and Turkey is essentially a secular state.[51]

Istanbul the capital of Turkey, eastern tourist city.

© Seqoya/Shutterstock.com

The Ottoman Empire collapsed after the end WWII. A World War II man named Ataturk created the modern state of Turkey. He proclaimed Turkey to be a secular state where Islam would play a minor role in the country's affairs. He also moved the capital from Istanbul to Ankara, an another example of a forward capital. Ataturk thought that coastal Istanbul was too prone to outside attack, and a more inward location would be more strategic. Also, Istanbul is technically on the European mainland, whereas most of Turkey is in Asia.[52] Turkey is one of the few transcontinental countries in the world. The Bosporus Strait is another key choke point in the region and crucial for political relations.

Picturesque mosque underneath volcano Damavand, highest peak in Iran

© Michal Knitl/Shutterstock.com

Iran is an oil-rich state between the Caspian Sea and the Persian Gulf. It has the second largest concentration of oil reserves in the region and is a theocracy. A **theocracy** refers to a place where government and religion interwine, main political figure in Iran is the leading Shiite cleric. Iran is strongly anti-Israel and has aspires to be a nuclear power. Iran has been closely involved in much of the region's turmoil and conflict.

In 2003, a large earthquake occurred in the ancient city of Bam, Iran, killing 27,000 people and destroying 75 percent of the city's buildings, including its ancient mud-citadel, the largest adobe building in the world. Bam was an oasis in the desert of the Iranian high plateau, dating back to the sixth century B.C.E. Bam's fortified settlement and citadel were developed at the crossroads of the silk and cotton trade routes.[54]

Cyprus, an island in the eastern Mediterranean Sea, is split between the European region and the Southwest Asian region. The eastern half of the island is ruled by Turkish Cypriots but recognized internationally only by Turkey.

Review Terms

Abraham	ISIS	North Africa
Arab Spring	Jerusalem	Orthodox branch
Arabian Peninsula	Jesus Christ	poaching
choke point	Kurds	Quran
Conservative branch	Levant	Reformed branch
Darfur	Mecca	Shiite
Empire States	Medina	Southwest Asia
failed state	Mesopotamia	Sunni
Far East	Middle East	Suez Canal
Fertile Crescent	Muhammad	The Maghreb
Five Pillars of Faith	Near East	theocracy
Hezbollah	Nile River	Western Wall

Research Topics

Arab League
caliphate
cultural diffusion
cultural landscape
domestication
environmental determinism
expansion diffusion
fossil fuel
fragmented modernization
hajj
hydraulic civilization
jihad
pastoral nomadism
religious revivalism
relocation diffusion
salinization
Sharia law
water stress

Credits

1. **Source:** From Thomas J. Karwoski, *World Regional Geography: An Introduction*, 1st ed., Copyright © 2016 by Kendall Hunt Publishing Company. Reprinted by permission

2. **Source:** From Thomas J. Karwoski, *World Regional Geography: An Introduction*, 1st ed., Copyright © 2016 by Kendall Hunt Publishing Company. Reprinted by permission

3. **Source:** From Thomas J. Karwoski, *World Regional Geography: An Introduction*, 1st ed., Copyright © 2016 by Kendall Hunt Publishing Company. Reprinted by permission

4. **Source:** From Thomas J. Karwoski, *World Regional Geography: An Introduction*, 1st ed., Copyright © 2016 by Kendall Hunt Publishing Company. Reprinted by permission

5. **Source:** From Alan A. Lew, C. Michael Hall, and Dallen J. Timothy, *World Regional Geography: Human Mobilities, Tourism, Destinations, Sustainable Environments*, 2nd ed., Copyright © 2015 by Kendall Hunt Publishing Company. Reprinted by permission.

6. **Source:** From Alan A. Lew, C. Michael Hall, and Dallen J. Timothy, *World Regional Geography: Human Mobilities, Tourism, Destinations, Sustainable Environments*, 2nd ed., Copyright © 2015 by Kendall Hunt Publishing Company. Reprinted by permission.

7. **Source:** From Alan A. Lew, C. Michael Hall, and Dallen J. Timothy, *World Regional Geography: Human Mobilities, Tourism, Destinations, Sustainable Environments*, 2nd ed., Copyright © 2015 by Kendall Hunt Publishing Company. Reprinted by permission.

8. **Source:** From Alan A. Lew, C. Michael Hall, and Dallen J. Timothy, *World Regional Geography: Human Mobilities, Tourism, Destinations, Sustainable Environments*, 2nd ed., Copyright © 2015 by Kendall Hunt Publishing Company. Reprinted by permission.

9. **Source:** From Alan A. Lew, C. Michael Hall, and Dallen J. Timothy, *World Regional Geography: Human Mobilities, Tourism, Destinations, Sustainable Environments*, 2nd ed., Copyright © 2015 by Kendall Hunt Publishing Company. Reprinted by permission.

10. **Source:** From Alan A. Lew, C. Michael Hall, and Dallen J. Timothy, *World Regional Geography: Human Mobilities, Tourism, Destinations, Sustainable Environments*, 2nd ed., Copyright © 2015 by Kendall Hunt Publishing Company. Reprinted by permission.

11. **Source:** From Thomas J. Karwoski, *World Regional Geography: An Introduction*, 1st ed., Copyright © 2016 by Kendall Hunt Publishing Company. Reprinted by permission.

12. **Source:** From Thomas J. Karwoski, *World Regional Geography: An Introduction*, 1st ed., Copyright © 2016 by Kendall Hunt Publishing Company. Reprinted by permission.

13. **Source:** From Thomas J. Karwoski, *World Regional Geography: An Introduction*, 1st ed., Copyright © 2016 by Kendall Hunt Publishing Company. Reprinted by permission.

14. **Source:** From Thomas J. Karwoski, *World Regional Geography: An Introduction*, 1st ed., Copyright © 2016 by Kendall Hunt Publishing Company. Reprinted by permission.

15. **Source:** From Thomas J. Karwoski, *World Regional Geography: An Introduction*, 1st ed., Copyright © 2016 by Kendall Hunt Publishing Company. Reprinted by permission.

16. **Source:** From Thomas J. Karwoski, *World Regional Geography: An Introduction*, 1st ed., Copyright © 2016 by Kendall Hunt Publishing Company. Reprinted by permission.

17. **Source:** From Thomas J. Karwoski, *World Regional Geography: An Introduction*, 1st ed., Copyright © 2016 by Kendall Hunt Publishing Company. Reprinted by permission.

18. **Source:** From Thomas J. Karwoski, *World Regional Geography: An Introduction*, 1st ed., Copyright © 2016 by Kendall Hunt Publishing Company. Reprinted by permission.

19. **Source:** From Thomas J. Karwoski, *World Regional Geography: An Introduction*, 1st ed., Copyright © 2016 by Kendall Hunt Publishing Company. Reprinted by permission.

20. **Source:** From Thomas J. Karwoski, *World Regional Geography: An Introduction*, 1st ed., Copyright © 2016 by Kendall Hunt Publishing Company. Reprinted by permission.

21. **Source:** From Thomas J. Karwoski, *World Regional Geography: An Introduction*, 1st ed., Copyright © 2016 by Kendall Hunt Publishing Company. Reprinted by permission.

22. **Source:** From Thomas J. Karwoski, *World Regional Geography: An Introduction*, 1st ed., Copyright © 2016 by Kendall Hunt Publishing Company. Reprinted by permission.

23. **Source:** From Thomas J. Karwoski, *World Regional Geography: An Introduction*, 1st ed., Copyright © 2016 by Kendall Hunt Publishing Company. Reprinted by permission.

24. **Source:** From Thomas J. Karwoski, *World Regional Geography: An Introduction*, 1st ed., Copyright © 2016 by Kendall Hunt Publishing Company. Reprinted by permission.

25. **Source:** From Thomas J. Karwoski, *World Regional Geography: An Introduction*, 1st ed., Copyright © 2016 by Kendall Hunt Publishing Company. Reprinted by permission.

26. **Source:** From Thomas J. Karwoski, *World Regional Geography: An Introduction*, 1st ed., Copyright © 2016 by Kendall Hunt Publishing Company. Reprinted by permission.

27. **Source:** From Thomas J. Karwoski, *World Regional Geography: An Introduction*, 1st ed., Copyright © 2016 by Kendall Hunt Publishing Company. Reprinted by permission.

28. **Source:** From Alan A. Lew, C. Michael Hall, and Dallen J. Timothy, *World Regional Geography: Human Mobilities, Tourism, Destinations, Sustainable Environments*, 2nd ed., Copyright © 2015 by Kendall Hunt Publishing Company. Reprinted by permission.

29. **Source:** From Thomas J. Karwoski, *World Regional Geography: An Introduction*, 1st ed., Copyright © 2016 by Kendall Hunt Publishing Company. Reprinted by permission.

30. **Source:** From Thomas J. Karwoski, *World Regional Geography: An Introduction*, 1st ed., Copyright © 2016 by Kendall Hunt Publishing Company. Reprinted by permission.

31. **Source:** From Thomas J. Karwoski, *World Regional Geography: An Introduction*, 1st ed., Copyright © 2016 by Kendall Hunt Publishing Company. Reprinted by permission.

32. **Source:** From Thomas J. Karwoski, *World Regional Geography: An Introduction*, 1st ed., Copyright © 2016 by Kendall Hunt Publishing Company. Reprinted by permission.

33. **Source:** From Thomas J. Karwoski, *World Regional Geography: An Introduction*, 1st ed., Copyright © 2016 by Kendall Hunt Publishing Company. Reprinted by permission.

34. **Source:** From Thomas J. Karwoski, *World Regional Geography: An Introduction*, 1st ed., Copyright © 2016 by Kendall Hunt Publishing Company. Reprinted by permission.

35. **Source:** From Thomas J. Karwoski, *World Regional Geography: An Introduction*, 1st ed., Copyright © 2016 by Kendall Hunt Publishing Company. Reprinted by permission.

36. **Source:** From Thomas J. Karwoski, *World Regional Geography: An Introduction*, 1st ed., Copyright © 2016 by Kendall Hunt Publishing Company. Reprinted by permission.

37. **Source:** From Thomas J. Karwoski, *World Regional Geography: An Introduction*, 1st ed., Copyright © 2016 by Kendall Hunt Publishing Company. Reprinted by permission.

38. **Source:** From Thomas J. Karwoski, *World Regional Geography: An Introduction*, 1st ed., Copyright © 2016 by Kendall Hunt Publishing Company. Reprinted by permission.

39. **Source:** From Thomas J. Karwoski, *World Regional Geography: An Introduction*, 1st ed., Copyright © 2016 by Kendall Hunt Publishing Company. Reprinted by permission.

40. **Source:** From Thomas J. Karwoski, *World Regional Geography: An Introduction*, 1st ed., Copyright © 2016 by Kendall Hunt Publishing Company. Reprinted by permission.

41. **Source:** From Thomas J. Karwoski, *World Regional Geography: An Introduction*, 1st ed., Copyright © 2016 by Kendall Hunt Publishing Company. Reprinted by permission.

42. **Source:** From Thomas J. Karwoski, *World Regional Geography: An Introduction*, 1st ed., Copyright © 2016 by Kendall Hunt Publishing Company. Reprinted by permission.

43. **Source:** From Thomas J. Karwoski, *World Regional Geography: An Introduction*, 1st ed., Copyright © 2016 by Kendall Hunt Publishing Company. Reprinted by permission.

44. **Source:** From Thomas J. Karwoski, *World Regional Geography: An Introduction*, 1st ed., Copyright © 2016 by Kendall Hunt Publishing Company. Reprinted by permission.

45. **Source:** From Thomas J. Karwoski, *World Regional Geography: An Introduction*, 1st ed., Copyright © 2016 by Kendall Hunt Publishing Company. Reprinted by permission.

46. **Source:** From Thomas J. Karwoski, *World Regional Geography: An Introduction*, 1st ed., Copyright © 2016 by Kendall Hunt Publishing Company. Reprinted by permission.

47. **Source:** From Thomas J. Karwoski, *World Regional Geography: An Introduction*, 1st ed., Copyright © 2016 by Kendall Hunt Publishing Company. Reprinted by permission.

48. **Source:** From Thomas J. Karwoski, *World Regional Geography: An Introduction*, 1st ed., Copyright © 2016 by Kendall Hunt Publishing Company. Reprinted by permission.

49. **Source:** From Thomas J. Karwoski, *World Regional Geography: An Introduction*, 1st ed., Copyright © 2016 by Kendall Hunt Publishing Company. Reprinted by permission.

50. **Source:** From Thomas J. Karwoski, *World Regional Geography: An Introduction*, 1st ed., Copyright © 2016 by Kendall Hunt Publishing Company. Reprinted by permission.

51. **Source:** From Thomas J. Karwoski, *World Regional Geography: An Introduction*, 1st ed., Copyright © 2016 by Kendall Hunt Publishing Company. Reprinted by permission.

52. **Source:** From Thomas J. Karwoski, *World Regional Geography: An Introduction*, 1st ed., Copyright © 2016 by Kendall Hunt Publishing Company. Reprinted by permission.

53. **Source:** From Thomas J. Karwoski, *World Regional Geography: An Introduction*, 1st ed., Copyright © 2016 by Kendall Hunt Publishing Company. Reprinted by permission.

54. **Source:** From Alan A. Lew, C. Michael Hall, and Dallen J. Timothy, *World Regional Geography: Human Mobilities, Tourism, Destinations, Sustainable Environments*, 2nd ed., Copyright © 2015 by Kendall Hunt Publishing Company. Reprinted by permission.

Chapter 11

SUB-SAHARAN AFRICA

Up until 1959, Africa was dominated by colonial powers. And by the colonial powers of Europe having complete control over Africa, they projected Africa always in a negative light—jungles, savages, cannibals, nothing civilized.

—Malcolm X

Where is Sub-Saharan Africa?

The region of Sub-Saharan Africa includes the lands south of the Sahara Desert. This region sits on the continent of Africa and touches each of Earth's hemispheres—Northern, Southern, Eastern, and Western. It resides on the African tectonic plate and the minor Somali tectonic plate.

The continent of Africa.

© boreala/Shutterstock.com

Sub-Saharan Africa versus North Africa

Significant climate, population, language, religion, and economic contrasts exist between North Africa and Sub-Saharan Africa. Dry climate conditions occur in North Africa, with most areas receiving less than 12 inches of annual precipitation. Humid climates are found in Sub-Saharan Africa, which receives 20–100 inches of precipitation annually.

Most of North Africa is sparsely populated, due to the largely dry climates. Sub-Saharan Africa is much more populated, with dense concentrations in the west and east. The Afro-Asiatic language family is used in North Africa while the Niger-Congo language family is used south of the Sahara. Islam is the major religion in

North Africa, and Christianity and tribal religions are practiced in Sub-Saharan Africa. Middle income countries appear in North Africa while low income countries make up Sub-Saharan Africa.

Major Qualities of Sub-Saharan Africa

Africa, especially Sub-Saharan Africa, is described as a plateau continent, its narrow coastal areas backed by steep escarpments, with most of land its a series of high plateaus. Every country in Africa is a multinational, multiethnic state, largely resulting from inefficient political boundaries created by European colonial empires. The culturally diverse political landscape leads to ethnic and religious conflicts, causing huge numbers of dislocated peoples and refugees.[2]

Waterberg plateau, Namibia
© GuilhermeMesquita/Shutterstock.com

Sub-Saharan Africa is the world's least economically developed region, with low incomes and low economic output. Most people engage in subsistence farming, a hallmark of low development. Over[3] one billion people inhabit the region that has the world's highest fertility rate. Another important characteristic of this region is that it has the world's highest concentration of endemic diseases, or diseases that are chronic or native to the area.[4]

Physical Geography[5]

Unlike Europe, the entire continent of Africa is compact. It has no large penetrating bays or seas. It is a relatively flat,[6] but high continent, with a generally uniform elevation and only a few high mountain regions.[7] Most of the land area in Sub-Saharan Africa is comprised of a series of high **plateaus** (elevated flat land), bordered by steep escarpments that lead down to narrow coastal plains. Most rivers originate on the plateaus and then tumble over the escarpments in steep waterfalls with rapids at the bottom. It is this distinctive topography that made Sub-Saharan Africa a "dark" continent. Reaching Sub-Saharan Africa meant either crossing the world's largest desert or ascending the steep escarpments. Europeans did not reach this area of the world until the late 1800s.

One of the most notable physiographic features seen from space satellites is the **Great Rift Valley,**[8] the largest rift valley in the world, averaging 30 miles wide and up to 3000 feet deep. (A rift valley is formed by a continent's splitting apart, moving each side of the valley in an opposite direction.)[9] In East Africa, faulting and plate movement created a set of valleys that filled with water to form a series of lakes and seas, such as Lake Victoria, Lake Malawi, the Red Sea, and the Dead Sea.[10]

Africa's largest tropical lowland is the **Congo Basin,**[11] the drainage basin for the Congo River,[12] the deepest river on earth. The Congo Basin is Africa's equivalent to South America's Amazon Basin. It lies astride the equator and is an extensive tropical rainforest with very warm, wet conditions.[13] The Congo River flows over a large number of waterfalls as it makes its way down from the higher fringes of the basin toward its center and out to the Atlantic Ocean. These waterfalls prevent navigation to the interior of the Congo, and along with ones in other basins, kept much of the interior of Africa a mystery.

In Southern Africa, the Kalahari Basin is an arid internal drainage basin. The rivers in this basin flow from higher elevations that receive more precipitation down toward the center of the basin, where they dissipate into the desert soils. (They do not flow out to the ocean[14] like most major rivers.)[15] In Zambia, the easterly flowing Zambezi River finds its headwaters and flows through Angola, Namibia, Botswana, Zimbabwe, and Mozambique on its way to the Indian Ocean. It drops in elevation multiple times as it tumbles over several waterfalls, including Victoria Falls, the collective largest waterfall in the world. Like many of the major rivers in Africa, it is vital for hydroelectric power in the region.

Sandstone Cliffs near Gesergio, Great Rift Valley, Ethiopia

© Oscar Espinosa/Shutterstock.com

Victoria Falls (Tokaleya Tonga: Mosi-oa-Tunya, "The Smoke that Thunders") is a waterfall in southern Africa on the Zambezi River at the border between Zambia and Zimbabwe.

© Yana Zubkova/Shutterstock.com

The Namib Desert is a tropical desert within Sub-Saharan Africa. It lies on the southwest coast of Africa, including most of the area of the countries of Namibia and Botswana. West Africa is the home of the Niger River, which flows through the arid Djouf Basin before it enters the Atlantic Ocean. The **Sahel**[16] is an arid region that lies along the southern margins of the Sahara[17] and includes the edge of the adjacent states of the Maghreb. It is a major transitional area with a mix of varied climates, religions, languages, and economies.[18] Here, Arab and Berber cultures from the north and African cultures from the south meet and interact with one another, sometimes in violent ways. Rainfall in the Sahel is very unpredictable due to the ITCZ, receiving adequate precipitation for agriculture and grazing in some years and severe droughts in others. Desertification, caused by the southward expansion of the Sahara, has become a serious problem. Overgrazing does not allow enough vegetation to regenerate. These problems intensify with the increasing population pressures in the region, and all of the countries along the Sahel have experienced famines over the last several decades.[19]

Exceptions to Africa's plateau topography are the Cape Range in South Africa, a major source of gold and diamonds; and Mount Kilimanjaro, a [20] standalone, extinct volcano and Africa's highest peak at 19,340 feet.[21]

Mount Kilimanjaro and clouds line at sunset, view from savanna landscape in Amboseli, Kenya, Africa

© PHOTOCREO Michal Bednarek/Shutterstock.com

History and Population[22]

Anthropologists believe Sub-Saharan Africa to be the place of origin for humankind. It has been the most impoverished region of the world, and poverty and short-life expectancies are continuing challenges for much of the region. It was almost completely controlled by different European powers during the colonial era.[23] Its plateau continent nature prevented the Europeans from arriving until the late 1800s. In 1884, most of the largest European countries met **Berlin Conference** and divided Africa into a series of European colonies. The Europeans were interested in acquiring important minerals and plantation crops. They used their economic motives to divide Africa without much consideration for native cultures, languages, and religions. These actions resulted in a distinctive set of political boundaries that separated the European colonies in Africa. **Superimposed boundaries** are boundaries drawn by outside interests with little regard to local cultures. These boundaries create largely multiethnic and multinational states that result in much political and cultural instability. Every country in Africa is a multinational state,[24] but most are not nation-states, and their citizens have not had a long history of identification with

The African policy of Europe.

© John Kehly/Shutterstock.com

today's African countries. To many Africans, the family, the clan, and the tribe are more important than either the individual or the country in which they live. European-drawn political states have little relation to traditional tribal boundaries.[25] Most countries within Sub-Saharan Africa obtained their independence in the 1950s and 1960s. Ghana, in West Africa, was the first African country to gain independence from Europe after World War II.[26]

Today, Sub-Saharan Africa has a significantly lower population density than many other areas of the world. Its population of about one million is approximately 13 percent of the world's population, relatively low, given the large land area that Sub-Saharan Africa encompasses. However, the current growth rate of 2.3 percent and other demographic change lead the UN to predict that the region will have a population of near 1.5 billion by 2050. It is also one of the poorest regions in the world, accounting for little more than one percent of the world's gross domestic product (GDP.)[27] **Subsistence agriculture** is the dominant economic activity in Sub-Saharan Africa. Most people are poor farmers, growing crops grazeing animals for their own needs, with little market orientation.[28]

Slavery

All of Sub-Saharan Africa's empires and kingdoms were in decline when the Europeans arrived in the sixteenth century. The major product Europeans wanted from was human. Slavery existed in Sub-Saharan Africa since Egyptian times. Arab traders sold Black slaves to the Greeks and Romans; early Greece had more slaves than free men. Slavery was also common in Sub-Saharan Africa itself, and it existed there long after it was abolished elsewhere in the world. Slavery still exists in pockets of Sub-Saharan Africa to this day.[29]

Sculpture of slaves dedicated to victims of slavery in Stone Town of Zanzibar

© Yakov Oskanov/Shutterstock.com

Slave Trade Scene from Guinea Bissau.

© Georgios Kollidas/Shutterstock.com

In the late sixteenth century, the Portuguese brought African slaves to work on the first plantations in the New World. Brazil was an area with low native population density, so the Portuguese relied on imported labor to work their agricultural lands. In 1602, the Dutch brought the first African slaves to Middle America, putting them to work in their Caribbean colonies. The first Africans came to the British colonies as indentured servants in 1619, a year before the Mayflower brought the Pilgrims to New England. The British were the main source's of African slaves in their colonies. They brought fabrics, costume jewelry, and other manufactured goods to West Africa, which they traded for slaves. They also brought corn, peanuts, sweet potatoes, coconuts, bananas, and citrus fruit (from other tropical lands) to Africa, all of which greatly improved the traditional diet of Sub-Saharan Africa. From West Africa, they brought slaves to the West Indies (the Caribbean) and to the colonial southern USA. Only 85 percent of the captured people survived the trans-Atlantic journey. (This number is much higher than in East Africa, though, where only 10 percent survived the Arab slave trade.) In total, an estimated 11 million[30] (some research says closer to 14 million) slaves were brought to the Americas.[31]

The African Diaspora forcibly migrated Africans across the Atlantic Ocean (1500s–1800s)

© Valery Sidelnykov/Shutterstock.com

In 1807, Great Britain banned slavery in the British Isles and, by 1834, throughout the British Empire. The United States banned the slave trade in 1808, though it was not enforced until after the Civil War. The slave trade last more than 200 years, both the plantations of the New World and because of the competitive nature of African tribes. Competition for scarce resources has long been an issue in Sub-Saharan Africa. Killing one's enemies gave way to enslaving them or selling them as slaves to others.[32]

Medical Geography

The hot, wet conditions that are common in most of Sub Saharan Africa are excellent environments for organisms like flies and mosquitos that carry and transmit many diseases. **Medical geography** studies the origin and diffusion of such diseases.

Medical researchers commonly categorize three types of diseases: endemic, epidemic, and pandemic. An **endemic disease** is chronic to a local area. It is omnipresent, physically weakening people exposed to it. Few people die from an endemic disease, but it zaps energy, lowers resistance, and helps to shorten lives. An endemic

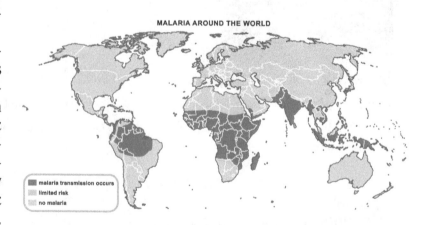

Malaria disease around the world.

© Peteri/Shutterstock.com

disease diffuses slowly, leading to local concentrations. Hepatitis and hookworm are examples of endemic diseases in Sub-Saharan Africa.

An **epidemic disease** breaks out suddenly and spreads rapidly at a regional scale. Many deaths result. Sleeping sickness is an epidemic disease in Sub-Saharan Africa. A **pandemic disease** spreads rapidly and globally with many deaths. Malaria and HIV/AIDS are examples of pandemic diseases.

Research highly suggests that HIV/AIDS is a disease that likely originated in the eastern Congo River basin as an endemic disease. It was probably chronic to this local area over a long period of time. The HIV virus appar-

10% of Ghana's population are orphans, due to HIV/AIDS.

© atm2003/Shutterstock.com

ently began in chimpanzees and eventually spread to people. HIV/AIDS became an epidemic disease through[33] **contagious diffusion** (spreading through population) along the main Congo highway via intravenous drug use and sexual activity. Over time, people from equatorial Africa migrated, creating a pandemic disease. Though HIV/AIDS originated in the Congo basin, Southern Africa currently has the highest rates of the disease.[34]

The overall impact of HIV/AIDS reduced the population of Sub-Saharan African by 70 million people by the year 2018 according to researchers. This includes the people who would have been born if it were not for the deaths of women of childbearing age. This number is more than twice the 30 million Europeans (one-third of the population at the time) who died of the bubonic plague (1347–1352 AD), which was previously considered the worst outbreak of disease in world history.[35]

Language and Religion[36]

Today, Africa is the most culturally and ethnically diverse region in the world. The world **tribe** is often used to describe the social organization in Sub-Saharan Africa. It refers to any group of people who share the same customs and languages, and who believe they descend from the same common ancestor. An estimated 600 to 1,000 tribes, many of which speak their own separate language, and an estimated 900 to 1,500 languages exist across Sub-Saharan Africa, and most Africans speak more than one language.[37] The Bantu is the largest and most widespread language group within the Niger-Congo language family and dominates in Sub-Saharan Africa. The Bantu originated in western Africa and eventually dispersed throughout central and southern Africa, becoming the most extensive group in the region.

The Khoisan language family is used in southwestern Africa. This language family once covered most of central and southern Africa. Today, only several thousand people, mainly Bushmen, speak it. The Khoisan language features a distinctive "clicking type" sound.

Christianity prevails throughout most of Sub-Saharan Africa, mixed with a variety of traditional tribal religions,[38] although, Islam touches the edges of the Sahel in the northern reaches of the continent and various countries in the region.

The Sub-Saharan African Region

Sub-Saharan Africa consists of seven subregions: Southern Africa, East Africa, Equatorial Africa, West Africa,[39] Madagascar and Mauritius, and the Sahel.[40]

Southern Africa

Southern Africa is the region's most economically developed area. Extensive, and diverse minerals and agricultural crops and relatively significant European settlement, are major reasons for the higher level of development. Southern Africa includes Angola, Namibia, Zambia, Zimbabwe, Mozambique,[41] Malawi, Botswana, Lesotho, Eswatini, and South Africa. The island country of Comoros is also part of this subregion.

A group of indigenous people seated in the bushmen village of Grashoek, Namibia.

© Gimas/Shutterstock.com

Angola is a former Portuguese colony[42] with excellent natural resources (oil, gold, copper, diamonds) that support the economy. The country also includes the exclave of Cabinda, which is north of the country and separated from it by the Democratic Republic of Congo (DRC).

Namibia is a former protectorate of South Africa. It includes most of the Namib Desert, the basis for the country's name. Namibia also includes most of the Bushmen, who speak the Khoisan language.[43]

Zambia and Zimbabwe are former British colonies originally known as Northern and Southern Rhodesia. Zimbabwe has encountered much political and ethnic instability, leading to major economic and political turmoil.

Mozambique is a former Portuguese colony with extensive deposits of bauxite, the ore from which aluminum comes.[44] The year 2019 saw two different tropical

Cyclone Idai heading towards Mozambique and Zimbabwe in 2019

© lavizzara/Shutterstock.com

cyclones hit the country. More than 1,000 people were killed in the cyclones that landed only a month apart, and millions have been displaced due to the destruction and flooding.

Malawi is a landlocked country, formally known as Nyasaland. Its economy is tied to agriculture and is one of the poorest less developed countries in the world.

Botswana is a landlocked country that is home to the Kalahari Desert. It has been severely impacted by the HIV/AIDs epidemic. Its economy is tied to diamonds and metals, including gold, nickel, and copper.

Lesotho is not only landlocked, but it is also an **enclaved** country (completely surrounded by another country) within South Africa. Controlled by the British for one hundred years, it became independent in 1966. Like Eswatini, it is home to several endemic species of mammals.

Eswatini is a landlocked country, that a name change. Until 2018, it was known for fifty years as Swaziland. The people are Swazis and that is also the language they speak. **Polygamy** (being married to more than one person at a time) is legal in this little country, as it is in multiple countries throughout the continent.

Maletsunyane Falls in Lesotho, Africa.

© mbrand85/Shutterstock.com

South Africa is Southern Africa's most populated country. It contains a wide array of important minerals, including coal, iron, uranium, gold, and diamonds. South Africa is the region's leading country in income and development. Historically, two main European groups settled in South Africa: the

Table Mountain, Cape Town, South Africa.

© Matthew Slade/Shutterstock.com

Dutch and the British. The Dutch lived in the interior, and the British became concentrated in the south around Cape Town. The descendants of the original Dutch settlers are known as the Boers or **Afrikaners**, assumed political control of the country in the mid 1900s, and instituted the apartheid policy. **Apartheid** was a policy of racial separation, especially subjecting the African population to widespread discrimination. Africans were forced to live in isolated, remote areas known as homelands. Over time, two of these former homelands became separate countries: Lesotho and Swaziland (now called Eswatini.)[45]

South Africa is a classic multinational, multiethnic state with four main diverse groups: Africans, Coloreds, Europeans, and South Asians. Africans comprise about 80 percent of the country's population. The Africans include a wide variety of tribal and language groups, including the Zulu and the Xhosa. The Coloreds are a mixed group of Africans and Whites, concentrated in the Cape Town area. The Europeans comprise less than 10 percent of the population, divided between the Afrikaners and the British. The smallest group is the South Asian population, descended from people of South and Southeast Asia. They were brought in by the Dutch and the British as domestics and laborers.[46]

Comoros is an island archipelago country off the eastern side of the Southern Africa subregion. Three main islands make up the primary land territory, two of which are volcanic, although only one is still active. The economy is known for spices and essential oils.

East Africa

East Africa includes much of the Great Rift Valley landscape. Most of the sub region is in the tropics but includes many highland areas that were attractive to European settlement. East Africa includes countries such as Kenya,[47] Burundi, Tanzania, Uganda, Rwanda, Ethiopia, Djibouti, Eritrea, and Somalia – the last four of which are often considered countries in the **Horn of Africa** (the far eastern edge of the Africa that juts into the Indian Ocean and Arabian Sea.) The island country of Seychelles is also covered in this subregion. Kenya is the major country in East Africa. It is the most populated country and contains relatively large numbers of European settlers. Nairobi is the capital of Kenya and the largest city in East Africa. Mombasa is Kenya's main port and the busiest in all of East Africa. Kenya also boasts the greatest concentration of big game reserves. Safaris and animal hunting are important components of the economy.[48]

Burundi is a landlocked country in the **African Great Lakes** region, (The lakes of the Great Rift Valley include

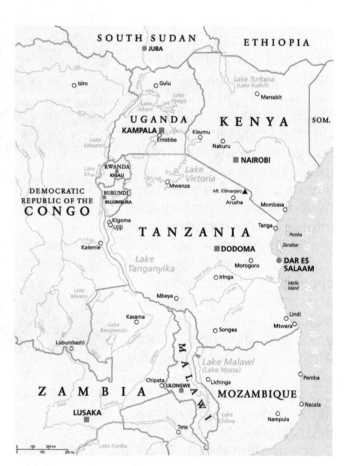

African Great Lakes.

© Peter Hermes Furian/Shutterstock.com

three of the largest freshwater lakes in the world. It was colonized by Germany and then Belgium. Today the population is mainly rural and has many environmental issues) caused by population pressures. It is the poorest country in the world, per 2019 research.

Tanzania is home to Mount Kilimanjaro, the Ngorongoro, and the Serengeti. It is famous for being home to an estimated 1.5 million large game herbivores and predators. Tourists whose goal it is to see the *Big Five animals*, named by hunters as the five most difficult animals to hunt,[49] bring much tourism to the region. The Big Five include the lion, the African elephant, the African buffalo, the leopard, and the black rhinoceros. These creatures are among the most dangerous in Africa, along with the hippopotamus, which considered the most dangerous animal when in water. Wildebeests, gazelles, and zebras are among the other big game animals that are distinctive to the safari lands of East and South Africa.[50]

Birds of Uganda - The Grey Crowned Crane
© Richardmak/Shutterstock.com

Uganda, like Kenya, is a former British colony. It was the country formerly led by brutal dictator Idi Amin. It had the longest running civil war on the continent. Uganda has had much success in using public health education programs aimed at reducing HIV/AIDS in yours people.[51]

Rwanda is a small country east of the Congo and south of Uganda. Two main tribes comprise the population of Rwanda: the Hutu and the Tutsi. The Hutu are the majority group in Rwanda. Primarily farmers, they are relatively short and squat in physique. The Tutsi are the minority group. They are mainly pastoralists (animal grazers) and are tall and more sophisticated in appearance. Under the Belgian rule, the Tutsis were a privileged minority. Over time, the Hutus became jealous of the privileges awarded the Tutsis and ridiculed them as "cockroaches." When Rwanda became independent, the government gave each citizen two items: a transistor radio and a machete. The transistor radios were intended to connect the citizens to the rest of the world, while the machete was meant to clear the tropical forests for crop or animal use. In April of 1994, the Hutu president attempted to fly to the neighboring country of Burundi. The plane carrying the president was shot down by a missile, killing him. Rumors quickly circulated, especially through Hutu radio disc jockeys, that the Tutsis were responsible. The disc jockeys then encouraged the Hutus to go home, get their machetes, and kill Tutsis in revenge. Ethnic cleansing ensued against Tutsis, young and old, male and female. Up to a million people died, with millions more becoming refugees.[52]

The house were ten UN Belgium soldiers were shot dead during the beginning of 1994 genocide in Ruanda.

© LMspencer/Shutterstock.com

Ethiopia's historic empire was the earliest major civilization of Sub-Saharan Africa, dating back to pre-Christian times. Ethiopia is a large country of East Africa. Legends indicate that the empire was founded by the son of King Solomon of Israel and the Queen of Sheba. Beta Jews from Ethiopia, who practiced a very old form of Judaism, have emigrated to Israel, based on an Israeli law that permits Jews from around the world to live in Israel.

The Ethiopian empire prospered through its trade with Arabs, supplying gold, ivory, and spices from inner Sub-Saharan Africa. During the nineteenth century, invading Italian forces defeated the Ethiopians and colonized the country in 1936. It was freed by a British invasion in 1941 in the early years of World War II. Today the highlands of Ethiopia are considered the Switzerland of Africa. with a Christian enclave surrounded by Islamic peoples. The lowland areas[53] though have been troubled by famine, war and civil unrest.[54]

Women from Surmi tribe, with flower decorations in Ethiopia.

© Luisa Puccini/Shutterstock.com

Djibouti is a country that sits where the three tectonic plates of Africa meet. The country has a range of topography with mountains and deserts, as well as grasslands. Another country in the Horn of Africa, it is known for great biodiversity including coral reef in the Red Sea off its coast.

Eritrea and Somalia[55], in the Horn of Africa, have been slow to develop, due to their lawlessness, war, terrorism, kidnappings and piracy.[56] Eritrea consists of the mainland and the more than one hundred islands in Dahlak

Red roofs of Eden Island, Seychelles.

© GagliardiPhotography/Shutterstock.com

Archipelago a Eritrea became independent in 1993, but the Eritrean People's Liberation Front (the country's one-party government) took control, has never held an election, and rules with a totalitarian dictator.

Somalia is located on the far eastern Horn of Africa. Over 85 percent of the people are Somalis, making the population quite homogeneous. Most people practice Islam and are Sunni Muslims. The country sits on the equator.

Seychelles is an island archipelago with granite and coral islands in the Indian Ocean off the coast of the East Africa subregion. It has been independent since 1976 and is a republic with the British Commonwealth. Many of the coral islands are in danger of being destroyed.

Equatorial Africa

Equatorial Africa is the least economically developed subregion in Sub-Saharan[57] Africa and includes the following countries: Sao Tome and Principe, the Central African Republic, the Democratic Republic of Congo (DRC), the Republic of Congo, Gabon, Cameroon, Equatorial Guinea, and South Sudan. It is based on the Congo River basin and adjacent areas of central Africa. It has the highest concentration of endemic diseases in Sub-Saharan Africa, poor soils, dense barrier forests, and much political and ethnic instability. The Ebola virus and HIV/AIDS originated in this area.

Sao Tome and Principe is an archipelago island country sitting off the west coast of Equatorial Africa. It has two archipelagos that were uninhabited when the Portuguese claimed them. Portuguese is the official language, and Roman Catholicism is the main religion.

The Central African Republic is a landlocked country that has been in a civil war for nearly eight years. It has tremendous natural resources and minerals, as well as arable agricultural lands. However, it is still one of the poorest countries in the world. Several rivers cross this country known for its savanna biome.

The Democratic Republic of Congo is a landlocked country that was once known as Zaire. It has prominent central location in Africa and is the second largest country in Africa by area. Like other equatorial countries, it has great natural resources but suffers from political corruption. Child malnutrition and starvation are common in this country, and many of its residents have emigrated to neighboring countries for a better life.

The Republic of Congo should not be confused with the DRC. Its capital city of Brazzaville sits on the northern banks of the massive Congo River, with a view of Kinshasa the capital of the DRC. The country is home to several national parks that protect wildlife like gorillas, chimpanzees, and elephants.

Gabon is dissected by the equator and has tremendous amounts of rainforest. The country is also known for its karst topography and protected national parks. Its economy is tied mainly to oil.

Gabon jungle

© Ivanov Gleb/Shutterstock.com

Cameroon sits on the west coast of the center of Africa, just north of the equator. Its official languages are French and English. It has a mix of biomes with desert land, mountains, savannas, and rainforest.

Equatorial Guinea is a little country nestled between Cameroon and Gabon on the coast of the Atlantic Ocean. Its territory also includes the five small Elobey islands and the Great Elobey island. The Fang is the largest ethnic group on the mainland, and most of the country practice Christianity.

South Sudan is a landlocked country that has existed only since its creation in 2011, when nearly 99 percent of the population voted for independence. Toward the end of 2013, civil war broke out, and the United Nations (UN) has tried to bring peace, but conflict continues to erupt and over 400,000 people have died in the fighting. The genocide of the Murle tribe is another tragedy in the region that is also known for high rates of child marriage.

West Africa

West Africa is the most populated sub-region in Sub-Saharan Africa. It is the homeland of the Bantu and the site of early agriculture, urbanization, and political empires. West Africa includes Senegal, the Gambia, Guinea, Togo, Benin, Guinea-Bissau, Cape Verde, Sierra Leone, Liberia, Ivory Coast, Ghana, and Nigeria.[58]

Senegal is the northernmost of the West African countries. It sits along the Sahel, and two-thirds of the country is desert or semiarid climate. Senegal differs from many of the countries further south in this region and is classified as a tropical savanna.

The Gambia is known for being the smallest mainland country in Africa. It touches only the country of Senegal and the Atlantic Ocean. The Gambia River dissects the country in half with its east-to-west flowing river.

Guinea is an Islamic, French-speaking country. It has rich natural resources, including diamonds, gold, and bauxite (the main export). The country made medical news in 2014 bats infected an 18-month-old boy with Ebola. It spread to Liberia and Sierra Leone.

Togo, or the Togolese Republic, and Benin are both small neighboring countries sitting on what has been called the slave coast of Africa. Benin has had many governmental changes since its independence in 1960, while Togo had

A South Sudanese soldier carries a machine gun in Paloch.

© punghi/Shutterstock.com

Republic of the Gambia is split in half by the Gambia River.

© pavalena/Shutterstock.com

Ebola epidemic in West Africa put the world on alert from 2013–2016.

© EFKS/Shutterstock.com

the same dictator for thirty-eight years. People tend to live closer to the coastal areas in both countries, as the far northern tip, close to the Sahel of Africa, is much drier.

Guinea-Bissau is a small country on the western edge of Africa, with a population of nearly two million people. The country sits at a low elevation, its highest point 984 feet.

Cape Verde is an island archipelago off the coast of the Western African subregion. Its ten volcanic islands were uninhabited when the Portuguese arrived in the mid-1400s. The islands are split into two groups and make a V-shaped pattern.

Sierra Leone is a small country on the west coast of Africa.[59] Its capital city of Freetown has a significant natural harbor that negatively impacted it during the trans-Atlantic slave trade. It was created to be a homeland for freed former British slaves,[60] and its official language is English. It is known for its **blood diamonds**[61] (name for diamonds mined in a war zone, also called conflict diamonds) that lead the country's economy. It also has a history of coups and civil wars. The 2014 Ebola virus greatly affected Sierra Leone[62], with over 3,700 cases and 1,200 deaths.

Freetown, Sierra Leone slums of the city

© robertonencini/Shutterstock.com

Liberia is another small country on the west coast of Africa. It was created to be a homeland for freed former American slaves[63] who wanted to return to Africa. The coastline of Liberia has mangrove trees that help reduce coastal erosion.

The Ivory Coast (Cote d'Ivoire) is located east of Liberia. It is a former French colony. In the 1980s, a Catholic president constructed a massive, hugely expensive basilica to rival St. Peter's in Vatican City. The basilica was built in the president's home town of Yamoussoukro in the interior, which became a forward capital that relocated from the former capital of Abidjan on the coast.

Ghana, once known as the Gold Coast,[64] sits along the Gulf of Guinea. It is divided by the Prime Meridian, so it is in both the Western and Eastern Hemispheres. Its close proximity to the equator gives it two main seasons, wet and dry, which is typical for areas in the ITCZ.

Nigeria is the most populated country in all of Africa[65] with a population of over two hundred million people. It is the region's leading oil producer. The original capital was Lagos, on the coast. Abuja, in the interior, is the more recent forward capital and[66] is centrally located in this compact shape country. Nigeria is another well-known illustration of a multiethnic, multinational state. It has three main ethnic groups: the Hausa, the Yoruba, and the Ibo. The Hausa dominate in the north, the Yoruba in the southwest, and the Ibo in the southeast.[67]

Madagascar and Mauritius

Madagascar is an island country, sitting 250 miles off the eastern coast of the Southern African countries. One main island and several smaller islands make up the lands of Madagascar. The island is known for great biodiversity with many endemic plants and animals, although they are environmentally at risk. Madagascar's people are not tied to Africa but to the ethnicities of people in Southeast Asia.

Mauritius is an island country east of Madagascar that has been controlled by Dutch, French, and British colonial powers. It includes one main island and few small islands. It was endemic home of the Dodo bird (extinct) and Mauritian Flying Fox (vulnerable).

The Sahel

The Sahel is a transitional area that extends west to east along the southern margins of the Sahara. The north is characterized by Islam, Arabic languages, dry climates, animal grazing, and lighter-skinned people. The south has Christianity, Bantu languages, humid climates, agriculture, and darker-skinned people. It is a fractious, turbulent area ethnic, religious, and political instability. It is also one of the world's most overpopulated and rapidly growing areas, with great poverty and[68] numerous environmental issues.[69] It includes the southern portions of the adjacent states of the Maghreb that were covered in Chapter 10: Mauritania, Mali, Burkina Faso, Niger, Chad, and quite a bit of the Sudan, as well.

Baobab Alley, Madagascar

© Gil.K/Shutterstock.com

The dodo (Raphus cucullatus) is an extinct flightless bird that was endemic to the island of Mauritius.

© life_in_a_pixel/Shutterstock.com

The Sahara desert and Sahel dividing line

© Rainer Lesniewski/Shutterstock.com

Review Terms

African Great Lakes
Afrikaners
apartheid
Berlin Conference
blood diamonds
Congo Basin
contagious diffusion
East Africa
enclaved

endemic disease
epidemic disease
Equatorial Africa
Great Rift Valley
Horn of Africa
medical geography
pandemic disease
plateau
polygamy

Sahel
Southern Africa
South Sudan
subsistence agriculture
superimposed boundaries
tribe
West Africa

Research Topics

alienated land
biofuel
Boko Haram
formal economy
informal economy
internally displaced
person
kleptocracy
land tenure
malaria
pastoralist
polyglots
refugee
state formation
steppe
swidden
Tsetse fly
xenophobia

China's Belt and Road Initiative in Africa

Cathleen Fritz, May 2019

CHINA'S BELT AND ROAD INITIATIVE IN AFRICE, MAY 2019

Contributed by Cathleen Fritz. © Kendall Hunt Publishing Company

The continent of Africa is rich in oil, iron ore, timber, gold, diamonds, and many other natural resources. Over the last two decades, Africans have seen a new "scramble" for economic development opportunities in their continent. The "scramble"

(Continued)

is between many African countries and China. This is a complex issue because the continent of Africa finally cut their ties to being colonized. The decolonization of Africa began in the 1950s and ended in the late 1970s. They had been dominated by Europe in the nineteenth and twentieth century. Much of Africa, except Ethiopia and Liberia, experienced European dominance. They fought hard to build democracies and stand on their own again. They intended to end being colonized forever.

Now? China is appealing to many African countries to build . . . . Build . . . . BUILD! The quest that is discussed by many political scholars and economists is whether Africa is being recolonized . . . Again. China has built many infrastructures like trains, roads, bridges, and seaports for shipping and trade, water and sewer systems to support migration to the cities, energy systems to power the new cities and corporations, and broadband internet to link all people, corporations, and governments to the economic development. China's Belt and Road Initiative in Africa is meant to serve the people of Africa and China. Who is funding all of these projects? China!

Read a few of the initiatives and then decide whether the African countries are benefitting from this growth as much as China.

1. China has funded two railways projects: Addis Ababa Light Rail Transit and Ethiopia-Djibouti Railway.
2. China built an African Union headquarters in Addis Ababa Ethiopia.
3. China is building a West African Union (ECOWAS) headquarters in Abuja Nigeria.
4. China is paying Guana for bauxite exploration and mining.
5. China is building a hydropower plant in Dondo, Angola, and Guinea.
6. China is building Special Economic Zone in the Congo.
7. China is building an oil refinery in Nigeria.
8. China is building a cement factory in Zambia.
9. China is building a residential district, an industrial zone, schools, a university, and recreational centers in Egypt.
10. China built a new parliament building in Harare, Zimbabwe.

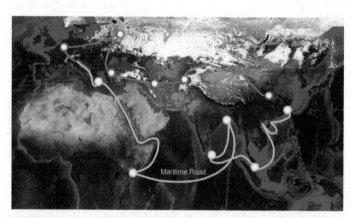

One belt one road route map.

© YIUCHEUNG / Shutterstock.com

All of these investments have cost China billions of dollars but the investment may be worth it if Africa generates financial gains for China. Is all of this building creating financial gains for Africa too? Do your research. You decide.

Credits

1. **Source:** From Thomas J. Karwoski, *World Regional Geography: An Introduction,* 1st ed., Copyright © 2016 by Kendall Hunt Publishing Company. Reprinted by permission.

2. **Source:** From Thomas J. Karwoski, *World Regional Geography: An Introduction,* 1st ed., Copyright © 2016 by Kendall Hunt Publishing Company. Reprinted by permission.

3. **Source:** From Thomas J. Karwoski, *World Regional Geography: An Introduction,* 1st ed., Copyright © 2016 by Kendall Hunt Publishing Company. Reprinted by permission.

4. **Source:** From Thomas J. Karwoski, *World Regional Geography: An Introduction,* 1st ed., Copyright © 2016 by Kendall Hunt Publishing Company. Reprinted by permission.

5. **Source:** From Thomas J. Karwoski, *World Regional Geography: An Introduction,* 1st ed., Copyright © 2016 by Kendall Hunt Publishing Company. Reprinted by permission.

6. **Source:** From Alan A. Lew, C. Michael Hall, and Dallen J. Timothy, *World Regional Geography: Human Mobilities, Tourism, Destinations, Sustainable Environments,* 2nd ed., Copyright © 2015 by Kendall Hunt Publishing Company. Reprinted by permission.

7. **Source:** From Alan A. Lew, C. Michael Hall, and Dallen J. Timothy, *World Regional Geography: Human Mobilities, Tourism, Destinations, Sustainable Environments,* 2nd ed., Copyright © 2015 by Kendall Hunt Publishing Company. Reprinted by permission.

8. **Source:** From Thomas J. Karwoski, *World Regional Geography: An Introduction,* 1st ed., Copyright © 2016 by Kendall Hunt Publishing Company. Reprinted by permission.

9. **Source:** From Alan A. Lew, C. Michael Hall, and Dallen J. Timothy, *World Regional Geography: Human Mobilities, Tourism, Destinations, Sustainable Environments,* 2nd ed., Copyright © 2015 by Kendall Hunt Publishing Company. Reprinted by permission.

10. **Source:** From Thomas J. Karwoski, *World Regional Geography: An Introduction,* 1st ed., Copyright © 2016 by Kendall Hunt Publishing Company. Reprinted by permission.

11. **Source:** From Thomas J. Karwoski, *World Regional Geography: An Introduction,* 1st ed., Copyright © 2016 by Kendall Hunt Publishing Company. Reprinted by permission.

12. **Source:** From Alan A. Lew, C. Michael Hall, and Dallen J. Timothy, *World Regional Geography: Human Mobilities, Tourism, Destinations, Sustainable Environments,* 2nd ed., Copyright © 2015 by Kendall Hunt Publishing Company. Reprinted by permission.

13. **Source:** From Thomas J. Karwoski, *World Regional Geography: An Introduction,* 1st ed., Copyright © 2016 by Kendall Hunt Publishing Company. Reprinted by permission.

14. **Source:** From Alan A. Lew, C. Michael Hall, and Dallen J. Timothy, *World Regional Geography: Human Mobilities, Tourism, Destinations, Sustainable Environments,* 2nd ed., Copyright © 2015 by Kendall Hunt Publishing Company. Reprinted by permission.

15. **Source:** From Alan A. Lew, C. Michael Hall, and Dallen J. Timothy, *World Regional Geography: Human Mobilities, Tourism, Destinations, Sustainable Environments,* 2nd ed., Copyright © 2015 by Kendall Hunt Publishing Company. Reprinted by permission.

16. **Source:** From Thomas J. Karwoski, *World Regional Geography: An Introduction,* 1st ed., Copyright © 2016 by Kendall Hunt Publishing Company. Reprinted by permission.

17. **Source:** From Thomas J. Karwoski, *World Regional Geography: An Introduction,* 1st ed., Copyright © 2016 by Kendall Hunt Publishing Company. Reprinted by permission.

18. **Source:** From Thomas J. Karwoski, *World Regional Geography: An Introduction,* 1st ed., Copyright © 2016 by Kendall Hunt Publishing Company. Reprinted by permission.

19. **Source:** From Alan A. Lew, C. Michael Hall, and Dallen J. Timothy, *World Regional Geography: Human Mobilities, Tourism, Destinations, Sustainable Environments,* 2nd ed., Copyright © 2015 by Kendall Hunt Publishing Company. Reprinted by permission.

20. **Source:** From Alan A. Lew, C. Michael Hall, and Dallen J. Timothy, *World Regional Geography: Human Mobilities, Tourism, Destinations, Sustainable Environments,* 2nd ed., Copyright © 2015 by Kendall Hunt Publishing Company. Reprinted by permission.

21. **Source:** From Alan A. Lew, C. Michael Hall, and Dallen J. Timothy, *World Regional Geography: Human Mobilities, Tourism, Destinations, Sustainable Environments,* 2nd ed., Copyright © 2015 by Kendall Hunt Publishing Company. Reprinted by permission.

22. **Source:** From Thomas J. Karwoski, *World Regional Geography: An Introduction,* 1st ed., Copyright © 2016 by Kendall Hunt Publishing Company. Reprinted by permission.

23. **Source:** From Alan A. Lew, C. Michael Hall, and Dallen J. Timothy, *World Regional Geography: Human Mobilities, Tourism, Destinations, Sustainable Environments,* 2nd ed., Copyright © 2015 by Kendall Hunt Publishing Company. Reprinted by permission.

24. **Source:** From Thomas J. Karwoski, *World Regional Geography: An Introduction,* 1st ed., Copyright © 2016 by Kendall Hunt Publishing Company. Reprinted by permission.

25. **Source:** From Alan A. Lew, C. Michael Hall, and Dallen J. Timothy, *World Regional Geography: Human Mobilities, Tourism, Destinations, Sustainable Environments,* 2nd ed., Copyright © 2015 by Kendall Hunt Publishing Company. Reprinted by permission.

26. **Source:** From Thomas J. Karwoski, *World Regional Geography: An Introduction,* 1st ed., Copyright © 2016 by Kendall Hunt Publishing Company. Reprinted by permission.

27. **Source:** From Alan A. Lew, C. Michael Hall, and Dallen J. Timothy, *World Regional Geography: Human Mobilities, Tourism, Destinations, Sustainable Environments,* 2nd ed., Copyright © 2015 by Kendall Hunt Publishing Company. Reprinted by permission.

28. **Source:** From Thomas J. Karwoski, *World Regional Geography: An Introduction,* 1st ed., Copyright © 2016 by Kendall Hunt Publishing Company. Reprinted by permission.

29. **Source:** From Alan A. Lew, C. Michael Hall, and Dallen J. Timothy, *World Regional Geography: Human Mobilities, Tourism, Destinations, Sustainable Environments,* 2nd ed., Copyright © 2015 by Kendall Hunt Publishing Company. Reprinted by permission.

30. **Source:** From Alan A. Lew, C. Michael Hall, and Dallen J. Timothy, *World Regional Geography: Human Mobilities, Tourism, Destinations, Sustainable Environments,* 2nd ed., Copyright © 2015 by Kendall Hunt Publishing Company. Reprinted by permission.

31. **Source:** From Alan A. Lew, C. Michael Hall, and Dallen J. Timothy, *World Regional Geography: Human Mobilities, Tourism, Destinations, Sustainable Environments,* 2nd ed., Copyright © 2015 by Kendall Hunt Publishing Company. Reprinted by permission.

32. **Source:** From Alan A. Lew, C. Michael Hall, and Dallen J. Timothy, *World Regional Geography: Human Mobilities, Tourism, Destinations, Sustainable Environments,* 2nd ed., Copyright © 2015 by Kendall Hunt Publishing Company. Reprinted by permission.

33. **Source:** From Thomas J. Karwoski, *World Regional Geography: An Introduction,* 1st ed., Copyright © 2016 by Kendall Hunt Publishing Company. Reprinted by permission.

34. **Source:** From Thomas J. Karwoski, *World Regional Geography: An Introduction,* 1st ed., Copyright © 2016 by Kendall Hunt Publishing Company. Reprinted by permission.

35. **Source:** From Alan A. Lew, C. Michael Hall, and Dallen J. Timothy, *World Regional Geography: Human Mobilities, Tourism, Destinations, Sustainable Environments,* 2nd ed., Copyright © 2015 by Kendall Hunt Publishing Company. Reprinted by permission.

36. **Source:** From Thomas J. Karwoski, *World Regional Geography: An Introduction,* 1st ed., Copyright © 2016 by Kendall Hunt Publishing Company. Reprinted by permission.

37. **Source:** From Alan A. Lew, C. Michael Hall, and Dallen J. Timothy, *World Regional Geography: Human Mobilities, Tourism, Destinations, Sustainable Environments,* 2nd ed., Copyright © 2015 by Kendall Hunt Publishing Company. Reprinted by permission.

38. **Source:** From Thomas J. Karwoski, *World Regional Geography: An Introduction,* 1st ed., Copyright © 2016 by Kendall Hunt Publishing Company. Reprinted by permission.

39. **Source:** From Thomas J. Karwoski, *World Regional Geography: An Introduction,* 1st ed., Copyright © 2016 by Kendall Hunt Publishing Company. Reprinted by permission.

40. **Source:** From Thomas J. Karwoski, *World Regional Geography: An Introduction,* 1st ed., Copyright © 2016 by Kendall Hunt Publishing Company. Reprinted by permission.

41. **Source:** From Thomas J. Karwoski, *World Regional Geography: An Introduction,* 1st ed., Copyright © 2016 by Kendall Hunt Publishing Company. Reprinted by permission.

42. **Source:** From Thomas J. Karwoski, *World Regional Geography: An Introduction,* 1st ed., Copyright © 2016 by Kendall Hunt Publishing Company. Reprinted by permission.

43. **Source:** From Thomas J. Karwoski, *World Regional Geography: An Introduction,* 1st ed., Copyright © 2016 by Kendall Hunt Publishing Company. Reprinted by permission.

44. **Source:** From Thomas J. Karwoski, *World Regional Geography: An Introduction,* 1st ed., Copyright © 2016 by Kendall Hunt Publishing Company. Reprinted by permission.

45. **Source:** From Thomas J. Karwoski, *World Regional Geography: An Introduction,* 1st ed., Copyright © 2016 by Kendall Hunt Publishing Company. Reprinted by permission.

46. **Source:** From Thomas J. Karwoski, *World Regional Geography: An Introduction,* 1st ed., Copyright © 2016 by Kendall Hunt Publishing Company. Reprinted by permission.

47. **Source:** From Thomas J. Karwoski, *World Regional Geography: An Introduction,* 1st ed., Copyright © 2016 by Kendall Hunt Publishing Company. Reprinted by permission.

48. **Source:** From Thomas J. Karwoski, *World Regional Geography: An Introduction,* 1st ed., Copyright © 2016 by Kendall Hunt Publishing Company. Reprinted by permission.

49. **Source:** From Alan A. Lew, C. Michael Hall, and Dallen J. Timothy, *World Regional Geography: Human Mobilities, Tourism, Destinations, Sustainable Environments,* 2nd ed., Copyright © 2015 by Kendall Hunt Publishing Company. Reprinted by permission.

50. **Source:** From Alan A. Lew, C. Michael Hall, and Dallen J. Timothy, *World Regional Geography: Human Mobilities, Tourism, Destinations, Sustainable Environments,* 2nd ed., Copyright © 2015 by Kendall Hunt Publishing Company. Reprinted by permission.

51. **Source:** From Thomas J. Karwoski, *World Regional Geography: An Introduction,* 1st ed., Copyright © 2016 by Kendall Hunt Publishing Company. Reprinted by permission.

52. **Source:** From Thomas J. Karwoski, *World Regional Geography: An Introduction,* 1st ed., Copyright © 2016 by Kendall Hunt Publishing Company. Reprinted by permission.

53. **Source:** From Alan A. Lew, C. Michael Hall, and Dallen J. Timothy, *World Regional Geography: Human Mobilities, Tourism, Destinations, Sustainable Environments,* 2nd ed., Copyright © 2015 by Kendall Hunt Publishing Company. Reprinted by permission.

54. **Source:** From Alan A. Lew, C. Michael Hall, and Dallen J. Timothy, *World Regional Geography: Human Mobilities, Tourism, Destinations, Sustainable Environments,* 2nd ed., Copyright © 2015 by Kendall Hunt Publishing Company. Reprinted by permission.

55. **Source:** From Alan A. Lew, C. Michael Hall, and Dallen J. Timothy, *World Regional Geography: Human Mobilities, Tourism, Destinations, Sustainable Environments,* 2nd ed., Copyright © 2015 by Kendall Hunt Publishing Company. Reprinted by permission.

56. **Source:** From Alan A. Lew, C. Michael Hall, and Dallen J. Timothy, *World Regional Geography: Human Mobilities, Tourism, Destinations, Sustainable Environments,* 2nd ed., Copyright © 2015 by Kendall Hunt Publishing Company. Reprinted by permission.

57. **Source:** From Thomas J. Karwoski, *World Regional Geography: An Introduction,* 1st ed., Copyright © 2016 by Kendall Hunt Publishing Company. Reprinted by permission.

58. **Source:** From Thomas J. Karwoski, *World Regional Geography: An Introduction,* 1st ed., Copyright © 2016 by Kendall Hunt Publishing Company. Reprinted by permission.

59. **Source:** From Thomas J. Karwoski, *World Regional Geography: An Introduction,* 1st ed., Copyright © 2016 by Kendall Hunt Publishing Company. Reprinted by permission.

60. **Source:** From Thomas J. Karwoski, *World Regional Geography: An Introduction,* 1st ed., Copyright © 2016 by Kendall Hunt Publishing Company. Reprinted by permission.

61. **Source:** From Thomas J. Karwoski, *World Regional Geography: An Introduction,* 1st ed., Copyright © 2016 by Kendall Hunt Publishing Company. Reprinted by permission.

62. **Source:** From Thomas J. Karwoski, *World Regional Geography: An Introduction,* 1st ed., Copyright © 2016 by Kendall Hunt Publishing Company. Reprinted by permission.

63. **Source:** From Thomas J. Karwoski, *World Regional Geography: An Introduction,* 1st ed., Copyright © 2016 by Kendall Hunt Publishing Company. Reprinted by permission.

64. **Source:** From Thomas J. Karwoski, *World Regional Geography: An Introduction,* 1st ed., Copyright © 2016 by Kendall Hunt Publishing Company. Reprinted by permission.

65. **Source:** From Thomas J. Karwoski, *World Regional Geography: An Introduction,* 1st ed., Copyright © 2016 by Kendall Hunt Publishing Company. Reprinted by permission.

66. **Source:** From Thomas J. Karwoski, *World Regional Geography: An Introduction,* 1st ed., Copyright © 2016 by Kendall Hunt Publishing Company. Reprinted by permission.

67. **Source:** From Thomas J. Karwoski, *World Regional Geography: An Introduction,* 1st ed., Copyright © 2016 by Kendall Hunt Publishing Company. Reprinted by permission.

68. **Source:** From Thomas J. Karwoski, *World Regional Geography: An Introduction,* 1st ed., Copyright © 2016 by Kendall Hunt Publishing Company. Reprinted by permission.

69. **Source:** From Thomas J. Karwoski, *World Regional Geography: An Introduction,* 1st ed., Copyright © 2016 by Kendall Hunt Publishing Company. Reprinted by permission.

Chapter 12

AUSTRALIA AND NEW ZEALAND

Where are Australia and New Zealand?

Australia and New Zealand are the most remote parts of the more developed world, located where the Pacific Ocean meets the Indian Ocean.[1] This region resides in the Southern and Eastern Hemispheres with Australia entirely on the Australian tectonic plate and New Zealand split between the Australian and the Pacific tectonic plates.

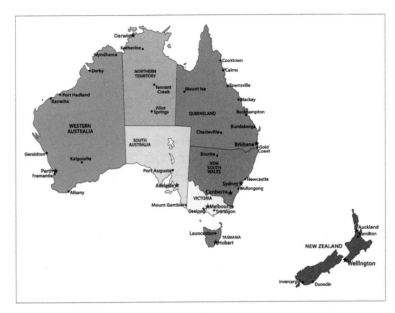

The Australia and New Zealand Region

© Serban Bogdan/Shutterstock.com

Major Qualities of Australia and New Zealand[2]

This region encompasses a vast area of relatively low population density; a lot of open water; and inhospitable deserts, rainforests, and fields of ice. These area is the most populated southern lands on the planet, with New Zealand (along with South America) being closest to Antarctica and the South Pole.[3] Both countries have been major colonial settlement areas for Europeans[4] as well.

Australia and New Zealand have been isolated from much of the rest of the world in recent geologic history, keep has produced unique flora.[5] These countries differ topographically and climatically. Australia has a vast, dry lowland interior, while New Zealand is more mountainous and has a more temperate climate. Climatically, most of Australia is dry, whereas New Zealand has a more temperate humid climate. Australia is continental in size; New Zealand is smaller in area. The region has an isolated location, relative to the rest of the more developed world, being on the remote periphery of the more developed states.

163

Both Australia and New Zealand have a peripheral pattern of population and urban settlement, with most urban populations highly clustered on the coasts. Australia has a population of 25 million people and[6] is primarily culturally European, with a small percentage of Asian and Aboriginal minorities[7]. New Zealand[8] has a population of almost 5 million people. Australia has a rapidly changing human geography, especially through newer sources of immigration. They each have political issues with indigenous populations.[9]

Commonalities of Australia and New Zealand

Australia and New Zealand share many common features, including a mainly British heritage and integration into the Pacific Rim economies of Asia. Both countries are highly developed economically well developed with high levels of urbanization. Australia and New Zealand share an excellent quality of life overall.

Challenges of distance and cost accompany their remote location. With small populations, they share small, internal domestic markets. Economically, they mainly export primary materials and import finished products with[10] far-removed remote external markets. Typically, more developed states import many raw materials and export finished products. Australia and New Zealand have a reversed trade pattern. They export raw materials and import finished products. Australia also exports wheat, beef, wool, and minerals, while New Zealand exports wool and dairy products. They both have unpredictable trade links with Asia.[11]

Merino in yards, every year millions of sheep are sold in sale yards all over the country for local consumption and international export from Australia.

© Alf Manciagli/Shutterstock.com

The Australian and New Zealand Region

Australia and New Zealand are the two states that comprise this region.

Australia

Australia is the dominant component of this region, in terms of both area and population.[12] Australia is the smallest continent in the world and the only continent to be controlled entirely by one country. About 25 million people inhabit Australia, making it one of the smallest more developed economies.[13] A major

Three Sisters, Blue Mountains, Australia

© Marc Witte/Shutterstock.com

Australia's Unique Flora and Fauna

In Australia, 95 percent of the fauna and 85 percent of the flora diversity are endemic, which means they are found only in Australia. Among Australia's native plants and animals, nonendemic species are mostly found in the northernmost part of the continent, having migrated there from Southeast Asia.

Among Australia's endemic animal species, 58 percent are placental mammals and 43 percent are marsupial mammals. Marsupials carry their offspring in pouches during some of their development. In Australia, there are marsupial mice, cats, anteaters, moles, wolves, marmots, wombats, dogs (Tasmanian devil), and koalas, in addition to the more distinctive wallabies and kangaroos.

Australian marsupial mammals: Wallaby, Tasmanian Devil, Wombat, Kangaroo with Joey, Quokka and Koala.

© Benny Marty / Shutterstock.com

limitation on Australia's population is the continent's low carrying capacity. Only 8 percent of Australia's land is **arable** (suitable for agriculture), and 1 percent is suited to intensive agriculture, such as that found in the central U.S. and in the Ukraine. Climate change profoundly affects Australia's agricultural production, as the country is getting warmer, and the change of low-frequency, high-magnitude weather events, such as floods and droughts, increases.[14]

Australia has the lowest average elevation and relief (change in elevation) of all the continents. Australia's highest mountains, the Great Dividing Range, extend along much of the east coast, with highest peaks reaching over 7,000 feet between Sydney and Melbourne. The older mountain systems have been heavily eroded, exposing considerable mineral wealth.[15] An advantage of the vast area of Australia is a rich array of mineral resources. Australia has gold, oil, natural gas, coal, iron ore, uranium, bauxite,[16] lead, zinc, and copper. Coal deposits are widespread and able to meet most of Australia's energy needs and are a significant, controversial export because of their contribution to carbon emissions.

The northern and northeastern parts of Australia have a rainforest climate, with occasional typhoons coming from the ITCZ along the equator. Air moves from east to west, so most of the tropical storms that hit Australia come across the Great Barrier Reef from the Coral Sea.[17]

Australia is a federal state, comprised of six states and two territories. The six states are Victoria, New South Wales, Queensland, South Australia, Western Australia, and Tasmania. The two territories are the Northern Territory and the Australian Capital Territory, including the federal capital city of Canberra.

Major architecture landmarks of the city of Sydney and the Sydney harbour.

© Taras Vyshnya/Shutterstock.com

Over 80 percent of the population is urbanized. Most of the population lives in scattered urban centers, principally on the southeast coast. Sydney and Melbourne are the two largest cities.[18]

The **Aborigines** are darker-skinned people who entered Australia about 50,000 years ago from Southeast Asia. Today, they are mainly concentrated in the **Outback**,[19] the dry interior of Australia that, largely comprises the Northern Territory[20] and the Simpson Desert, Great Sandy Desert and Great Victoria Desert.[21] Of Australia's total population, only 600,000 are Aborigines. They were greatly discriminated and were largely viewed as second-class citizens. Today they tend to be relatively poor, with higher levels of poverty and unemployment.[22] Australian Aborigines only became citizens in their own country in 1966 following a national referendum.[23] It wasn't until the 1990s that the Aborigines could claim title to traditional land.[24] Today, the Australian government has reparation programs for the Aboriginal people, who lost much of their traditional lands, and the country has become more accepting. Aboriginal land issues, continue especially in the

A Hakea tree stands alone in the Australian outback during sunset. Pilbara region, Western Australia, Australia.

© bmphotographer/Shutterstock.com

Outback, and the government is often regarded as racist because of its treatment of Aborigines and its policies toward illegal migrants or refugees.[25]

The first European settlers were British convicts who arrived in the late 1700s. British prisons had become overcrowded. Many excess prisoners used to be sent to the British colonies in North America; however, with the end of the American War for Independencey Britain had to look for alternate sites. Australia became the largest of these destinations[26] after 1776. Australian historian Robert Hughes described Australia as the world's first gulag. Later these penal colonies became known as free colonies after the prisoners had served their sentences.[27] In the early 1800s, more traditional British settlers and farmers arrived. In the 1900s, large numbers of Europeans from other parts of Europe began to immigrate. More recently, Asia has become a major new source area for Australian immigration.[28]

New Zealand

New Zealand is much smaller in land area and population than Australia. Its has major islands, the North Island and the South Island,[29] and both are mountainous. The North Island is mainly of volcanic origin, contains the largest city, Auckland, and includes the capital city of Wellington. It is more populated than the South Island[30] and has most of the flat farmland.[31] The South Island has been highly affected by glacial activity and is more mountainous than the North Island.[32] The mountains of South Island are referred to as the Southern Alps, reach over 12,000 feet, and are home to permanent glaciers. Human settlement is primarily in the coastal areas, due to the mountainous

Yirrganydji Aboriginal man plays music on a didgeridoo in Queensland, Australia.

© ChameleonsEye/Shutterstock.com

Port Arthur the old convict colony and historic jail located in Tasmania, Australia

© robdimagery/Shutterstock.com

Panorama of Milford Sound (Fjordland, New Zealand)

© Henner Damke/Shutterstock.com

interiors of the islands. New Zealand is further south than most of Australia and has a more humid Marine West Coast climate, with year-round rain fall.[33]

New Zealand lies on the Pacific Ring of Fire[34] and is an active volcanic, earthquake, and geothermal region. These geothermal phenomena provide geysers, volcanic calderas, mineral springs, and hot mud baths.[35] Less than[36] 5 million people live in New Zealand,[37] 75 percent of whom are of European origin.[38] The original inhabitants are the **Maori**, a people of Polynesian descent who arrived in New Zealand about 1,000 years ago. Today, they comprise about[39] 600,000 people, giving New Zealand a higher share of indigenous peoples, compared to Australia.[40] Maori people often use the term *tangata whenua*, meaning "people of the land," to describe their relationship with a particular area of the land. In 1769, Captain Cook claimed New Zealand for England, and Christian missionaries soon followed. Christianity and eventual acceptance of British law brought an end to the Maori intertribal warfare and cannibalism, although the New Zealand Maori land wars were not over until the 1870s. Reparations are still being sought and decided for the outcome of Maori land. Today there is considerable interracial harmony between the Maori and the European populations.[41]

New Zealand is home to a spectacular array of birds. Many of

Waitangi, New Zeland, North Island, - Maori warriors celebrating Waitangi Day, the anniversary of the treaty of Waitangi between the British government and the Maori.

© Umomos/Shutterstock.com

New Zealand, a little spotted kiwi.

© John Carnemolla/Shutterstock.com

which are now extinct or endangered, including some endemic flightless birds (kiwis and the extinct moas.) Numerous placental animals have been introduced, and sheep represent a major grazing animal in both countries, which are both leading exporters of sheep and wool. The introduction of domestic sheep, wild goats, wild pigs, and placental rats and mice have led to the loss of numerous animal and plant species in both countries.[42]

Review Terms

Aborigines	Australia	Outback
arable	Maori	

Research Topics

aboriginal land issues
APEC
desalinization
environmental degradation
Great Barrier Reef
intercropping
kanaka
marsupial
outback
peripheral development
primary sector
unitary state
viticulture

Credits

1. **Source:** From Thomas J. Karwoski, *World Regional Geography: An Introduction*, 1st ed., Copyright © 2016 by Kendall Hunt Publishing Company. Reprinted by permission.
2. **Source:** From Thomas J. Karwoski, *World Regional Geography: An Introduction*, 1st ed., Copyright © 2016 by Kendall Hunt Publishing Company. Reprinted by permission.
3. **Source:** From Alan A. Lew, C. Michael Hall, and Dallen J. Timothy, *World Regional Geography: Human Mobilities, Tourism, Destinations, Sustainable Environments*, 2nd ed., Copyright © 2015 by Kendall Hunt Publishing Company. Reprinted by permission.
4. **Source:** From Alan A. Lew, C. Michael Hall, and Dallen J. Timothy, *World Regional Geography: Human Mobilities, Tourism, Destinations, Sustainable Environments*, 2nd ed., Copyright © 2015 by Kendall Hunt Publishing Company. Reprinted by permission.
5. **Source:** From Alan A. Lew, C. Michael Hall, and Dallen J. Timothy, *World Regional Geography: Human Mobilities, Tourism, Destinations, Sustainable Environments*, 2nd ed., Copyright © 2015 by Kendall Hunt Publishing Company. Reprinted by permission.
6. **Source:** From Thomas J. Karwoski, *World Regional Geography: An Introduction*, 1st ed., Copyright © 2016 by Kendall Hunt Publishing Company. Reprinted by permission.
7. **Source:** From Alan A. Lew, C. Michael Hall, and Dallen J. Timothy, *World Regional Geography: Human Mobilities, Tourism, Destinations, Sustainable Environments*, 2nd ed., Copyright © 2015 by Kendall Hunt Publishing Company. Reprinted by permission.
8. **Source:** From Thomas J. Karwoski, *World Regional Geography: An Introduction*, 1st ed., Copyright © 2016 by Kendall Hunt Publishing Company. Reprinted by permission.
9. **Source:** From Thomas J. Karwoski, *World Regional Geography: An Introduction*, 1st ed., Copyright © 2016 by Kendall Hunt Publishing Company. Reprinted by permission.
10. **Source:** From Thomas J. Karwoski, *World Regional Geography: An Introduction*, 1st ed., Copyright © 2016 by Kendall Hunt Publishing Company. Reprinted by permission.
11. **Source:** From Thomas J. Karwoski, *World Regional Geography: An Introduction*, 1st ed., Copyright © 2016 by Kendall Hunt Publishing Company. Reprinted by permission.

12. **Source:** From Thomas J. Karwoski, *World Regional Geography: An Introduction*, 1st ed., Copyright © 2016 by Kendall Hunt Publishing Company. Reprinted by permission.

13. **Source:** From Thomas J. Karwoski, *World Regional Geography: An Introduction*, 1st ed., Copyright © 2016 by Kendall Hunt Publishing Company. Reprinted by permission.

14. **Source:** From Alan A. Lew, C. Michael Hall, and Dallen J. Timothy, *World Regional Geography: Human Mobilities, Tourism, Destinations, Sustainable Environments*, 2nd ed., Copyright © 2015 by Kendall Hunt Publishing Company. Reprinted by permission.

15. **Source:** From Alan A. Lew, C. Michael Hall, and Dallen J. Timothy, *World Regional Geography: Human Mobilities, Tourism, Destinations, Sustainable Environments*, 2nd ed., Copyright © 2015 by Kendall Hunt Publishing Company. Reprinted by permission.

16. **Source:** From Thomas J. Karwoski, *World Regional Geography: An Introduction*, 1st ed., Copyright © 2016 by Kendall Hunt Publishing Company. Reprinted by permission.

17. **Source:** From Alan A. Lew, C. Michael Hall, and Dallen J. Timothy, *World Regional Geography: Human Mobilities, Tourism, Destinations, Sustainable Environments*, 2nd ed., Copyright © 2015 by Kendall Hunt Publishing Company. Reprinted by permission.

18. **Source:** From Thomas J. Karwoski, *World Regional Geography: An Introduction*, 1st ed., Copyright © 2016 by Kendall Hunt Publishing Company. Reprinted by permission.

19. **Source:** From Thomas J. Karwoski, *World Regional Geography: An Introduction*, 1st ed., Copyright © 2016 by Kendall Hunt Publishing Company. Reprinted by permission.

20. **Source:** From Thomas J. Karwoski, *World Regional Geography: An Introduction*, 1st ed., Copyright © 2016 by Kendall Hunt Publishing Company. Reprinted by permission.

21. **Source:** From Alan A. Lew, C. Michael Hall, and Dallen J. Timothy, *World Regional Geography: Human Mobilities, Tourism, Destinations, Sustainable Environments*, 2nd ed., Copyright © 2015 by Kendall Hunt Publishing Company. Reprinted by permission.

22. **Source:** From Thomas J. Karwoski, *World Regional Geography: An Introduction*, 1st ed., Copyright © 2016 by Kendall Hunt Publishing Company. Reprinted by permission.

23. **Source:** From Alan A. Lew, C. Michael Hall, and Dallen J. Timothy, *World Regional Geography: Human Mobilities, Tourism, Destinations, Sustainable Environments*, 2nd ed., Copyright © 2015 by Kendall Hunt Publishing Company. Reprinted by permission.

24. **Source:** From Thomas J. Karwoski, *World Regional Geography: An Introduction*, 1st ed., Copyright © 2016 by Kendall Hunt Publishing Company. Reprinted by permission.

25. **Source:** From Alan A. Lew, C. Michael Hall, and Dallen J. Timothy, *World Regional Geography: Human Mobilities, Tourism, Destinations, Sustainable Environments*, 2nd ed., Copyright © 2015 by Kendall Hunt Publishing Company. Reprinted by permission.

26. **Source:** From Thomas J. Karwoski, *World Regional Geography: An Introduction*, 1st ed., Copyright © 2016 by Kendall Hunt Publishing Company. Reprinted by permission.

27. **Source:** From Alan A. Lew, C. Michael Hall, and Dallen J. Timothy, *World Regional Geography: Human Mobilities, Tourism, Destinations, Sustainable Environments*, 2nd ed., Copyright © 2015 by Kendall Hunt Publishing Company. Reprinted by permission.

28. **Source:** From Thomas J. Karwoski, *World Regional Geography: An Introduction*, 1st ed., Copyright © 2016 by Kendall Hunt Publishing Company. Reprinted by permission.

29. **Source:** From Thomas J. Karwoski, *World Regional Geography: An Introduction*, 1st ed., Copyright © 2016 by Kendall Hunt Publishing Company. Reprinted by permission.

30. **Source:** From Thomas J. Karwoski, *World Regional Geography: An Introduction*, 1st ed., Copyright © 2016 by Kendall Hunt Publishing Company. Reprinted by permission.

31. **Source:** From Alan A. Lew, C. Michael Hall, and Dallen J. Timothy, *World Regional Geography: Human Mobilities, Tourism, Destinations, Sustainable Environments*, 2nd ed., Copyright © 2015 by Kendall Hunt Publishing Company. Reprinted by permission.

32. **Source:** From Thomas J. Karwoski, *World Regional Geography: An Introduction*, 1st ed., Copyright © 2016 by Kendall Hunt Publishing Company. Reprinted by permission.

33. **Source:** From Alan A. Lew, C. Michael Hall, and Dallen J. Timothy, *World Regional Geography: Human Mobilities, Tourism, Destinations, Sustainable Environments*, 2nd ed., Copyright © 2015 by Kendall Hunt Publishing Company. Reprinted by permission.

34. **Source:** From Thomas J. Karwoski, *World Regional Geography: An Introduction*, 1st ed., Copyright © 2016 by Kendall Hunt Publishing Company. Reprinted by permission.

35. **Source:** From Alan A. Lew, C. Michael Hall, and Dallen J. Timothy, *World Regional Geography: Human Mobilities, Tourism, Destinations, Sustainable Environments*, 2nd ed., Copyright © 2015 by Kendall Hunt Publishing Company. Reprinted by permission.

36. **Source:** From Thomas J. Karwoski, *World Regional Geography: An Introduction*, 1st ed., Copyright © 2016 by Kendall Hunt Publishing Company. Reprinted by permission.

37. **Source:** From Thomas J. Karwoski, *World Regional Geography: An Introduction*, 1st ed., Copyright © 2016 by Kendall Hunt Publishing Company. Reprinted by permission.

38. **Source:** From Alan A. Lew, C. Michael Hall, and Dallen J. Timothy, *World Regional Geography: Human Mobilities, Tourism, Destinations, Sustainable Environments*, 2nd ed., Copyright © 2015 by Kendall Hunt Publishing Company. Reprinted by permission.

39. **Source:** From Thomas J. Karwoski, *World Regional Geography: An Introduction*, 1st ed., Copyright © 2016 by Kendall Hunt Publishing Company. Reprinted by permission.

40. **Source:** From Thomas J. Karwoski, *World Regional Geography: An Introduction*, 1st ed., Copyright © 2016 by Kendall Hunt Publishing Company. Reprinted by permission.

41. **Source:** From Alan A. Lew, C. Michael Hall, and Dallen J. Timothy, *World Regional Geography: Human Mobilities, Tourism, Destinations, Sustainable Environments*, 2nd ed., Copyright © 2015 by Kendall Hunt Publishing Company. Reprinted by permission.

42. **Source:** From Alan A. Lew, C. Michael Hall, and Dallen J. Timothy, *World Regional Geography: Human Mobilities, Tourism, Destinations, Sustainable Environments*, 2nd ed., Copyright © 2015 by Kendall Hunt Publishing Company. Reprinted by permission.

Chapter 13

OCEANIA

One might almost say that the history of geographical discovery, properly so called, begins with Captain Cook, the motive of whose voyages were purely scientific curiosity.

—Joseph Jacobs

Where is Oceania?

Oceania is comprised of tens of thousands of islands scattered over the Pacific Ocean.[1] This region resides in all four hemispheres, mainly south of the Tropic of Cancer and north of the Antarctic Circle. It resides on the Australian tectonic plate and the Pacific tectonic plate.

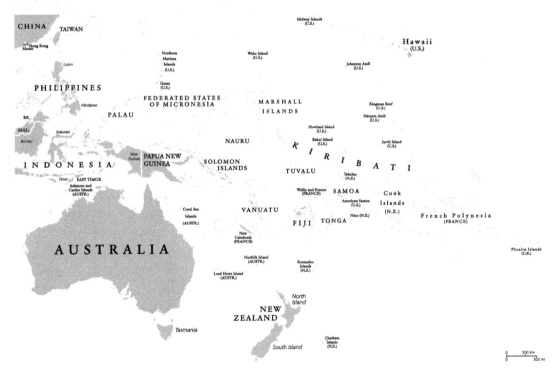

The Oceania Region includes Melanesia, Micronesia and Polynesia.

© Peter Hermes Furian/Shutterstock.com

Major Qualities of Oceania

Oceania is the largest of all world regions in territorial size, although it has the smallest land area and the smallest population. Nearly eleven million people live in Oceania. The peoples of this vast region share ethnicity and close relationships via water and ocean travel. Islands dominate Oceania, and it is a highly fragmented region, comprised of three island subregions of **Melanesia, Micronesia,** and **Polynesia.** The island of New Guinea, of which half is included in the region of Oceania, is the second-largest island in the world after Greenland. Papua New Guinea is also the most populated island, with over 70 percent of the region's population.

The term *South Pacific* is generally applied to the island microstates of the southern Pacific Ocean. The islands have few natural resources, except large ocean territories (fishing) and access to the three Ss: *sun, sea and sand*. The islands' isolation has resulted in substantial species endemism, dependence on the natural environment, diversity of cultures and language, and vulnerability to natural disasters. The region's colonial heritage means that states remain economically linked to their former colonial occupiers. The region's image as an island paradise is also a colonial legacy rather than an actual reality, given histories of occasional political unrest, poverty and natural disasters (cyclones and tsunamis.)

Beautiful view across the bay in the South Pacific

© Richard Vandewalle/Shutterstock.com

Oceania has been strongly affected by the United Nations Law of the Sea provisions concerning the rights of coastal states over adjacent waters. Oceania's islands are often divided into volcanic high islands versus coral-based low islands. **Volcanic high islands** are economically based on agriculture. High islands typically have a tall volcanic mountain in the center, causing the humid ocean winds to rise, forming clouds and precipitation. High islands have year-round rainfall (an important source of fresh water) and tropical rainforests. The populations are much larger on high islands because rainfall and rich volcanic soils can able to support agriculture.

Coral low islands are mainly oriented to fishing and contain smaller populations. Low islands are usually coral atolls. They were once high islands but were eroded away by wind, rain and waves, and the original shelled material eroded to form sandy stretches of land above the sea. Some of these are quite large, and they sometimes have a freshwater lagoon in their center. Their elevations are not as high, and they do not capture much precipitation from passing winds. They tend to be hotter and drier, with some exhibiting almost desert-like conditions. Many low islands are regarded as countries most vulnerable to climate change and sea level rise in the world.

United Nations Conferences on the Law of the Sea

Historically, the territorial sea referred to the ocean waters adjacent to a coastal state, where all the rights of a coastal state prevailed. The high seas were larger areas of the ocean, where everything was open to all. Over time, many disputes occurred as coastal states tried to claim various areas. From the 1950s to the 1980s, the United Nations convened several conferences on the law of the sea. In 1982, a Convention on the Law of the Sea established international guidelines for control of the oceans.

A **12-mile territorial sea** was established. Within this adjacent zone, a coastal state could exercise **sovereignty** or total control over all affairs. An **Exclusive Economic Zone** was established from 12–200 miles off a coastal state. Within this zone, coastal states could exercise limited economic rights over fishing and minerals. Beyond the 200-mile limit lay the **high seas**, open to one and all. The guidelines do not affect landlocked states nor do they effectively deal with issues where states are closer than 200 miles to each other. They do provide an international framework that standardizes areas of control to minimize future disputes.[17]

Some of the islands in Oceania have direct political connections to more developed countries, such as American Samoa and the United States. Nationals from Cook Islands, Niue, and Tokelau are also citizens of New Zealand, so their movement is legally and politically unrestricted. In addition, political unrest influenced some migration flows in this region, particularly of the Fijian Indian community.[18]

The Oceania Region

Oceania includes three subregions: Melanesia, Micronesia, and Polynesia.

Melanesia

Melanesia is a group of islands that lie northeast of Australia. The name refers to the darker skin of most of the residents.[19] The Negrito people were the earliest to settle in Oceania, predating the Malayo-Polynesia peoples. The Malayo-Polynesian people, or Austronesian people most likely migrated out of Taiwan, moving down through the Philippines and into insular Southeast Asia before spreading out into the Pacific. The Polynesians used stars (their height above the horizon) and ocean currents (by which they could also detect nearby islands) to navigate the vast waters of the Pacific Ocean.[20]

Melanesia is the most populous subregion in Oceania[21], with 10.6 million people. Melanesia includes Papua New Guinea, Solomon Islands, New Caledonia, Fiji, and[22] Vanuatu. Papua New Guinea is the most populated state in Oceania, with about[23] 8.5 million people. It became independent in the 1970s after a century

The men of the Huli tribe in Tari area of Papua New Guinea in traditional clothes and face paint.

© Amy Nichole Harris/Shutterstock.com

of British and Australian control. Papua New Guinea comprises the eastern half of the island of New Guinea,[24] the western half, known as Papua, is part of Indonesia and resides in Southeast Asia. Crude oil is now Papua New Guinea's leading export. There are also deposits of gold, copper, and silver that provide a diversity of resources.[25]

The Solomon Islands lie east of Papua New Guinea. Approximately 1,000 islands, most unoccupied, comprise the Solomon Islands.[26] Over 600,000 people live in the Solomon Islands. Numerous languages and physical fragmentation facilitate many conflicts for this area.[27] Political unrest, interethnic violence (between the Solomon Islanders and the ethnic Chinese), and natural disasters in recent years have all but curtailed tourism. The country has also appeared on warning lists throughout the world.[28]

New Caledonia is a French territory directly east of Australia.[29] Less than 300,000 people live in New Caledonia; about 35 percent of the population is of European ancestry, mainly French. Nickel is the main export.

Fiji is on the far eastern margin of Melanesia. It achieved independence in the 1970s. Approximately[30] 900,000 residents live on about 100 islands. Over 40 percent of the population is from South Asia, brought from India by the British to work on sugar plantations.[31] A non-violent coup in December 2007 effectively halted tourism to the islands for a few months, although it has since recovered. In September 2014, Fiji again became a parliamentary democracy following the first general election since the 2007 coup.[32]

Navala village in the Ba Highlands of northern-central Viti Levu, Fiji. It is one of the few settlements in Fiji, which remains fully traditional architecturally.

© ChameleonsEye/Shutterstock.com

Captain James Cook, 1728–1779

© Everett Historical/Shutterstock.com

Vanuatu is an archipelago of 80+ islands that were claimed by the Spanish, French, and British when the islands were still-called the New Hebrides by Captain Cook. There are several active volcanoes on the islands, but ironically the arable land is limited due to poor soil content.

Micronesia

Micronesia has more than 2,000[33] low-lying small islands that lie north of Melanesia and east of the Philippines. Subsistence farming and fishing support the economy, but most islands survive on foreign aid. Until the 1980s, Micronesia was largely a United States Trust Territory. Now it is comprised of the Marshall Islands, Northern Mariana Islands, Palau, Guam, Nauru, The Federated States of Micronesia, Kiribati, and Wake Island.

The Marshall Islands are in a free association with the United States. The United States tested nuclear weapons there in the mid-twentieth century. The Northern Mariana Islands is a commonwealth in political union with the United States. Billions of dollars are sent by the United States in assistance to these countries.

Palau is a series of islands east of the Philippines that became independent in the 1990s. It is dependent upon the United States for financial aid and military security. Guam is a United States territory where U.S. military installations and tourism provide most of the income.[34] It is the largest of the Micronesian islands.[35]

Green sea turtle, feeding in Palau

© jbutcher/Shutterstock.com

Wonderful underwater world - Jellyfish Lake, Palau.

© Divelvanov/Shutterstock.com

Nauru acquired wealth by exporting phosphate to Australia and New Zealand for use as fertilizer. Most of the main deposits have run out, causing much economic uncertainty.[36]

Like the Marshall Islands, the Federated States of Micronesia are independent but associated with the United States, although Spain still recognize its claim to a few of the islands. The over six hundred islands are divided into four main states: Yap, Chuuk, Pohnpei, and Kosrae (west to east).

Kiribati is made up of 30+ atolls and a coral island that is divided into three main groups for identification. It has a rich cultural heritage derived from the influence of invaders over the centuries.

Wake Island is a coral atoll of three islands. It is named after the British Captain William Wake but is an unincorporated, unorganized territory of the United States. The island is used to support the U.S. Air Force.

Scuba

The Micronesian islands, particularly Palau, the Federated States of Micronesia, Guam and the Marshall Islands, are well known for scuba diving, white sand, blue waters, and vast array of coral reefs. Some of the Micronesian island countries are also trying to establish heritage tourism based on their living cultures and World War II battle sites and memorials.[37]

Chuuk, Micronesia

© J.S. Lamy/Shutterstock.com

Polynesia

Polynesia lies to the east of Melanesia and Micronesia, as does the International Date Line. It forms a large triangle stretching from the Hawaiian Islands to Easter Island to New Zealand. These many islands vary from large volcanic islands to low coral atolls. The Polynesians have lighter skin and wavier hair than most of the other peoples of Oceania. Polynesia includes the islands of Tonga, Tuvalu, Tahiti, Samoa,[38] Cook Islands, American Samoa, Hawaii, Easter Island, Midway Islands, and the Pitcairn islands.

Tonga is a kingdom that became independent from the British in 1970. It lies southeast of Fiji[39] and comprises 169 islands, sometimes referred to as the "friendly islands" because of Cook's reception upon visiting.

Polynesian authentic and famous dish-raw fish salad with cucumber, lime, tomato and coconut milk.

© Dolly MJ/Shutterstock.com

Tuvalu gained its independence from the British in 1976,[40] when it was known as the Ellice Islands. It lies east of the Solomon Islands[41] and once were joined by the Gilbert Islands that make up an island group in Kiribati. Coconut is a staple in the Tuvaluan diet.

Bora Bora, French Polynesia

© Lukas Bischoff Photograph/Shutterstock.com

Tahiti is a French territory, part of the broader French Polynesia that also includes the Marquesas Islands and the Society Islands. Tourism is a mainstay of the economy.[42] Tahiti is the largest and highest island in the French Polynesian islands.

Samoa is located to the northeast of Fiji and Tonga. The eastern part of Samoa has become very Americanized in society and landscape.[43] Samoa is made up of two main islands and a few small islets as well.

Cook Islands are sometimes referred to as the New Zealand territories due to their foreign support and the fact that Cook Islanders are considered citizens of New Zealand. Named after Captain Cook, who visited the islands more than once on his tours, the islands are considering renaming themselves now to represent their historic culture. They were like many islands in Oceania, a British territory for several decades, and are typically split between their northern and southern islands.

American Samoa is another unincorporated territory of the United States. It is made up of five main islands and two coral atolls. It is known historically for being one of the only places on earth not impacted by the Spanish Influenza in 1918 due to a strict quarantine placed on it.

Hawaii is the most recently added state in the United States back in 1959. It is the only state not in the North American region and not residing on the North American tectonic plate. It consists of eight main islands, with Hawaii being the "Big Island."

Skyline of Honolulu, Hawaii and the surrounding area, including the hotels and buildings on Waikiki Beach.

© Izabela23/Shutterstock.com

Easter Island sits considerably east of its governing nation of Chile and is considered one of the most remote inhabited islands in the world. It is a volcanic high island known for its recognizable statues of the Moai.

Midway Islands or the Midway Atoll is an unorganized, unincorporated territory of the United States. It is part of the Hawaiian archipelago, but not under Hawaii's governing jurisdiction. It sits about midway from North America and Asia, and so is considered aptly named.

Moais in Rapa Nui National Park on the slopes of Rano Raruku volcano on Easter Island, Chile.

© Amy Nichole Harris/Shutterstock.com

Review Terms

12-mile territorial sea
coral low islands
Exclusive Economic Zone
high seas

Melanesia
Micronesia
Oceania
Polynesia

sovereignty
volcanic high islands

Research Topics

bikini atoll
continental shelf
equidistance principle
exclusive economic zone
lagoon
maritime boundary
Pidgin English
rising sea level
territorial sea

Credits

1. **Source:** From Thomas J. Karwoski, *World Regional Geography: An Introduction*, 1st ed., Copyright © 2016 by Kendall Hunt Publishing Company. Reprinted by permission.
2. **Source:** From Thomas J. Karwoski, *World Regional Geography: An Introduction*, 1st ed., Copyright © 2016 by Kendall Hunt Publishing Company. Reprinted by permission.
3. **Source:** From Thomas J. Karwoski, *World Regional Geography: An Introduction*, 1st ed., Copyright © 2016 by Kendall Hunt Publishing Company. Reprinted by permission.

4. **Source:** From Alan A. Lew, C. Michael Hall, and Dallen J. Timothy, *World Regional Geography: Human Mobilities, Tourism, Destinations, Sustainable Environments*, 2nd ed., Copyright © 2015 by Kendall Hunt Publishing Company. Reprinted by permission.

5. **Source:** From Thomas J. Karwoski, *World Regional Geography: An Introduction*, 1st ed., Copyright © 2016 by Kendall Hunt Publishing Company. Reprinted by permission.

6. **Source:** From Thomas J. Karwoski, *World Regional Geography: An Introduction*, 1st ed., Copyright © 2016 by Kendall Hunt Publishing Company. Reprinted by permission.

7. **Source:** From Alan A. Lew, C. Michael Hall, and Dallen J. Timothy, *World Regional Geography: Human Mobilities, Tourism, Destinations, Sustainable Environments*, 2nd ed., Copyright © 2015 by Kendall Hunt Publishing Company. Reprinted by permission.

8. **Source:** From Alan A. Lew, C. Michael Hall, and Dallen J. Timothy, *World Regional Geography: Human Mobilities, Tourism, Destinations, Sustainable Environments*, 2nd ed., Copyright © 2015 by Kendall Hunt Publishing Company. Reprinted by permission.

9. **Source:** From Alan A. Lew, C. Michael Hall, and Dallen J. Timothy, *World Regional Geography: Human Mobilities, Tourism, Destinations, Sustainable Environments*, 2nd ed., Copyright © 2015 by Kendall Hunt Publishing Company. Reprinted by permission.

10. **Source:** From Thomas J. Karwoski, *World Regional Geography: An Introduction*, 1st ed., Copyright © 2016 by Kendall Hunt Publishing Company. Reprinted by permission.

11. **Source:** From Thomas J. Karwoski, *World Regional Geography: An Introduction*, 1st ed., Copyright © 2016 by Kendall Hunt Publishing Company. Reprinted by permission.

12. **Source:** From Alan A. Lew, C. Michael Hall, and Dallen J. Timothy, *World Regional Geography: Human Mobilities, Tourism, Destinations, Sustainable Environments*, 2nd ed., Copyright © 2015 by Kendall Hunt Publishing Company. Reprinted by permission.

13. **Source:** From Thomas J. Karwoski, *World Regional Geography: An Introduction*, 1st ed., Copyright © 2016 by Kendall Hunt Publishing Company. Reprinted by permission.

14. **Source:** From Alan A. Lew, C. Michael Hall, and Dallen J. Timothy, *World Regional Geography: Human Mobilities, Tourism, Destinations, Sustainable Environments*, 2nd ed., Copyright © 2015 by Kendall Hunt Publishing Company. Reprinted by permission.

15. **Source:** From Thomas J. Karwoski, *World Regional Geography: An Introduction*, 1st ed., Copyright © 2016 by Kendall Hunt Publishing Company. Reprinted by permission.

16. **Source:** From Alan A. Lew, C. Michael Hall, and Dallen J. Timothy, *World Regional Geography: Human Mobilities, Tourism, Destinations, Sustainable Environments*, 2nd ed., Copyright © 2015 by Kendall Hunt Publishing Company. Reprinted by permission.

17. **Source:** From Thomas J. Karwoski, *World Regional Geography: An Introduction*, 1st ed., Copyright © 2016 by Kendall Hunt Publishing Company. Reprinted by permission.

18. **Source:** From Alan A. Lew, C. Michael Hall, and Dallen J. Timothy, *World Regional Geography: Human Mobilities, Tourism, Destinations, Sustainable Environments*, 2nd ed., Copyright © 2015 by Kendall Hunt Publishing Company. Reprinted by permission.

19. **Source:** From Thomas J. Karwoski, *World Regional Geography: An Introduction*, 1st ed., Copyright © 2016 by Kendall Hunt Publishing Company. Reprinted by permission.

20. **Source:** From Alan A. Lew, C. Michael Hall, and Dallen J. Timothy, *World Regional Geography: Human Mobilities, Tourism, Destinations, Sustainable Environments*, 2nd ed., Copyright © 2015 by Kendall Hunt Publishing Company. Reprinted by permission.

21. **Source:** From Thomas J. Karwoski, *World Regional Geography: An Introduction*, 1st ed., Copyright © 2016 by Kendall Hunt Publishing Company. Reprinted by permission.

22. **Source:** From Thomas J. Karwoski, *World Regional Geography: An Introduction*, 1st ed., Copyright © 2016 by Kendall Hunt Publishing Company. Reprinted by permission.

23. **Source:** From Thomas J. Karwoski, *World Regional Geography: An Introduction*, 1st ed., Copyright © 2016 by Kendall Hunt Publishing Company. Reprinted by permission.

24. **Source:** From Thomas J. Karwoski, *World Regional Geography: An Introduction*, 1st ed., Copyright © 2016 by Kendall Hunt Publishing Company. Reprinted by permission.

25. **Source:** From Thomas J. Karwoski, *World Regional Geography: An Introduction*, 1st ed., Copyright © 2016 by Kendall Hunt Publishing Company. Reprinted by permission.

26. **Source:** From Thomas J. Karwoski, *World Regional Geography: An Introduction*, 1st ed., Copyright © 2016 by Kendall Hunt Publishing Company. Reprinted by permission.
27. **Source:** From Thomas J. Karwoski, *World Regional Geography: An Introduction*, 1st ed., Copyright © 2016 by Kendall Hunt Publishing Company. Reprinted by permission.
28. **Source:** From Alan A. Lew, C. Michael Hall, and Dallen J. Timothy, *World Regional Geography: Human Mobilities, Tourism, Destinations, Sustainable Environments*, 2nd ed., Copyright © 2015 by Kendall Hunt Publishing Company. Reprinted by permission.
29. **Source:** From Thomas J. Karwoski, *World Regional Geography: An Introduction*, 1st ed., Copyright © 2016 by Kendall Hunt Publishing Company. Reprinted by permission.
30. **Source:** From Thomas J. Karwoski, *World Regional Geography: An Introduction*, 1st ed., Copyright © 2016 by Kendall Hunt Publishing Company. Reprinted by permission.
31. **Source:** From Thomas J. Karwoski, *World Regional Geography: An Introduction*, 1st ed., Copyright © 2016 by Kendall Hunt Publishing Company. Reprinted by permission.
32. **Source:** From Alan A. Lew, C. Michael Hall, and Dallen J. Timothy, *World Regional Geography: Human Mobilities, Tourism, Destinations, Sustainable Environments*, 2nd ed., Copyright © 2015 by Kendall Hunt Publishing Company. Reprinted by permission.
33. **Source:** From Thomas J. Karwoski, *World Regional Geography: An Introduction*, 1st ed., Copyright © 2016 by Kendall Hunt Publishing Company. Reprinted by permission.
34. **Source:** From Thomas J. Karwoski, *World Regional Geography: An Introduction*, 1st ed., Copyright © 2016 by Kendall Hunt Publishing Company. Reprinted by permission.
35. **Source:** From Alan A. Lew, C. Michael Hall, and Dallen J. Timothy, *World Regional Geography: Human Mobilities, Tourism, Destinations, Sustainable Environments*, 2nd ed., Copyright © 2015 by Kendall Hunt Publishing Company. Reprinted by permission.
36. **Source:** From Thomas J. Karwoski, *World Regional Geography: An Introduction*, 1st ed., Copyright © 2016 by Kendall Hunt Publishing Company. Reprinted by permission.
37. **Source:** From Alan A. Lew, C. Michael Hall, and Dallen J. Timothy, *World Regional Geography: Human Mobilities, Tourism, Destinations, Sustainable Environments*, 2nd ed., Copyright © 2015 by Kendall Hunt Publishing Company. Reprinted by permission.
38. **Source:** From Thomas J. Karwoski, *World Regional Geography: An Introduction*, 1st ed., Copyright © 2016 by Kendall Hunt Publishing Company. Reprinted by permission.
39. **Source:** From Thomas J. Karwoski, *World Regional Geography: An Introduction*, 1st ed., Copyright © 2016 by Kendall Hunt Publishing Company. Reprinted by permission.
40. **Source:** From Thomas J. Karwoski, *World Regional Geography: An Introduction*, 1st ed., Copyright © 2016 by Kendall Hunt Publishing Company. Reprinted by permission.
41. **Source:** From Thomas J. Karwoski, *World Regional Geography: An Introduction*, 1st ed., Copyright © 2016 by Kendall Hunt Publishing Company. Reprinted by permission.
42. **Source:** From Thomas J. Karwoski, *World Regional Geography: An Introduction*, 1st ed., Copyright © 2016 by Kendall Hunt Publishing Company. Reprinted by permission.
43. **Source:** From Thomas J. Karwoski, *World Regional Geography: An Introduction*, 1st ed., Copyright © 2016 by Kendall Hunt Publishing Company. Reprinted by permission.

Chapter 14

THE POLES AND OCEANS

We need to respect the oceans and take care of them as if our lives depended on it. Because they do.

—Sylvia Earle

Where Are the Poles?

The Poles are composed of two areas on Earth. The **North Pole** sits at 90° N latitude and includes the Arctic territory south to the **Arctic Circle** of 66.56° N. It resides on the Eurasian tectonic plate and the North American tectonic plate at the top of the Northern Hemisphere. The **South Pole** sits at 90° S latitude and includes the continental territory of Antarctica just slightly north of the **Antarctic Circle** at 66.56° S. It resides on the Antarctic tectonic plate at the base of the Southern Hemisphere.

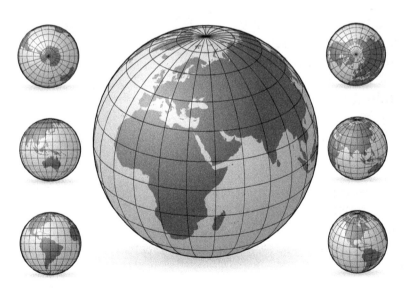

Latitudinal locations around the globe.

© Alfonso de Tomas/Shutterstock.com

183

Where Are the Oceans?

The oceans are composed of five major bodies of water: the **Pacific Ocean**, separating Asia and Australia from the North and South America; the **Atlantic Ocean**, separating North and South America from Europe and Africa; the **Indian Ocean**, separating Africa from the southern parts of Asia; the **Arctic Ocean**, separating Europe and Asia from North America; and the **Southern Ocean**, separating Antarctica from Australia, Africa, and South America.

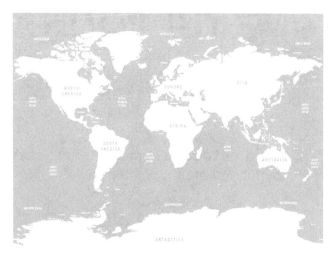

Oceanographical map of world

© Pyty/Shutterstock.com

The North Pole and the Arctic

The North Pole, from the concept of latitude, is the most northern place on Earth. Its surrounding southern land of the Arctic includes Russia, Finland, Sweden, Norway, Greenland, Canada, and the United States; however, the North Pole itself sits over the frozen waters of the Arctic Ocean, which can be up to several feet thick with shifting ice sheets. Each of these countries has a stake in the condition of the Arctic lands.

The territory north of the Arctic Circle experiences darkness for considerable amounts of time from December to March, and has vast amounts of light from June to September. The Winter

Pressure ridge and melt water at the Geographic North Pole

© Christopher Wood/Shutterstock.com

Solstice and Summer Solstice play a key role in daily routine for residents in its circumference. The same is true for those lands around the South Pole and Antarctica, except in opposite seasons and months.

Physical limitations and lack of demand, result in few roads, and most of them run only a few kilometers outside of regional towns. Travel in the far north is extremely expensive: short flights often cost thousands of dollars. Historically, only a few indigenous groups were known to have lived in the extreme northern conditions.

The South Pole and Antarctica

The South Pole, from the concept of latitude, is the most southern place on Earth. Its surrounding northern land of Antarctica includes the entire continent but no governed countries. Antarctica resides mainly south of the Antarctic Circle but juts out from its key line of latitude near South America, where the Antarctic Peninsula is found.

Antarctica is larger than Europe but has no human permanent population and only minimal forms of biological life. Massive sheets of ice and almost constant stormy seas kept Antarctica isolated from much of the rest of the world until the late 1700s. Antarctica remains a frontier region hostile to human habitation and is seldom visited, except by scientists and a small number of cruise passengers and adventure tourists.[1]

Ice covers nearly all of Antarctica; its average thickness is 7,000 to 8,000 feet, although, at its deepest, it is almost 3 miles thick. The ice sheets contain 90 percent of all the ice and 70 percent of all the fresh water in the world. Only 2 percent of Antarctica is ice-free; these small areas are known as oases and are located on the continent's edge. In winter, which is July in the southern hemisphere, the outer edge of the ice shelves can extend up to 1000 miles from the continent. The edges of these shelves periodically break off and float as icebergs northward toward warmer waters.[2]

The **Antarctic Convergence** is a zone located approximately 1,000 miles off the coast and is the transition area between the icy cold waters and the warmer ocean currents[3] of the Pacific, Atlantic, and Indian Oceans to the north. Also surrounding the continent is the Antarctic Circumpolar Current, which moves clockwise (eastward) around the continent and is the longest ocean current in the world. Antarctica has the world's lowest recorded temperature, –128.6° F. The average temperature in the interior is –70° F, while the warmest temperatures on the Antarctic Peninsula can reach as high as 59° F in the Antarctic summer. The interior of Antarctica is, in fact, a desert,[4] (as are the extreme northern lands in the Arctic) owing to the high pressure air system that resides over the South Pole. The average precipitation is only 1 to 2 inches of rainfall equivalent a year.

Twelve countries were part of the agreements to protect Antarctica's resources and preserve them for scientific use, which was codified in the 1959 **Antarctic Treaty**. These included Argentina, Australia,

Melting iceberg in Antarctica.

© spatuletail/Shutterstock.com

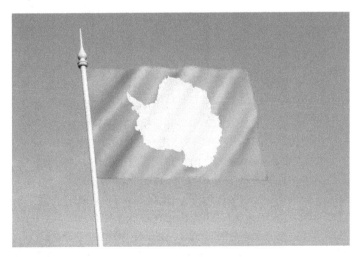

Antarctica has no official flag as it is not a nation or ruled by a single government. This is the most widely used flag - a map of the continent on a pale blue background that symbolizes neutrality.

© Steve Allen/Shutterstock.com

Belgium, Chile, France, Japan, New Zealand, Norway, South Africa, the United Kingdom, the United States, and Russia (the Soviet Union at that time.) The Antarctic Treaty allows military activities for scientific and peaceful purposes only. Other countries have since joined the Antarctic Treaty.[5]

Flora and Fauna

The limited plant and animal life in the extreme northern and southern areas of Earth include many species found only there. Some bacteria, lichens, and algae grow in the polar areas. Insects are the most abundant animal life. Several penguin species live in Antarctica, as well as four endemic species of seal[6], while polar bears, walrus, narwhals, and arctic fox are the larger species in the Arctic. Fish are quite abundant and have blood that enables them to live in waters as cold as 28° F. Krill is a small shrimp that exists in huge numbers in the icy waters and comprise the basic food for birds, seals, and whales.[7]

Gentoo Penguins run over the snow in Antarctica

© vladsilver/Shutterstock.com

Polar bear sow and cub walk on ice floe in Norwegian Arctic waters.

© FloridaStock/Shutterstock.com

Walrus and her pup floating on ice in a fjord in eastern Greenland.

© wildestanimal/Shutterstock.com

The Global Ocean

Humankind tends to emphasize the diversity of life and landscapes on the 29 percent of the earth that is continents and islands. However, most of the planet (71 percent) is actually covered by water, and oceans comprise 97 percent of that. The oceans are a major source of food for humans, accounting for approximately 10 percent of human protein consumption. They are also a very important medium for human migration, commercial transportation, and recreation and tourism. The shallower continental shelves have

Logistics and transportation ship

© Nok Nok/Shutterstock.com

also served as important sources for fossil fuel and mineral extraction, and recent research demonstrates the major role the oceans play in regulating climate change and directing its impact in some locations over others.[8]

Despite its substantial importance, much of the geography of the oceans remains unknown. New animal species and ways that the oceans impact the global climate are continually being discovered. Our lack of adequate knowledge of ocean ecosystems often results in human-caused environmental disasters, including oil spills, overfishing, and large-scale pollution.[9]

The Pacific Ocean

The Pacific Ocean is the largest of the five oceans, covering 28 percent of the planet (about the same as all of the land areas combined.) It has an average depth of 13,215 feet, and contains the deepest spot on[10] Earth: **Challenger Deep** in the Mariana Trench (near Guam.) That point is 35,840 feet below sea level. Most of the Pacific Ocean is surrounded by the Pacific Ring of Fire, where various oceanic and terrestrial tectonic plates are colliding, causing frequent earthquakes and volcanic and other mountain-building and island-creating activities.

Underwater earthquakes can result in large tsunami events, caused by a sudden shift in the ocean floor elevation that can flood island and coastal areas around the entire Pacific Ocean basin. A Pacific-wide tsunami warning system includes floating wave detectors (buoys) that help confirm whether if an earthquake-generated tsunami might threaten life and property.[11]

The Atlantic Ocean

About half the Pacific Ocean's size, the Atlantic Ocean is the second largest ocean. Unlike the Pacific Ocean, the Atlantic Ocean is an area where the major tectonic plates are moving away from each one another, with North and South America moving westward and away from Europe and Africa. The equator divides the Atlantic and Pacific Oceans into northern and southern portions.[12]

The Indian Ocean

The Indian Ocean is the third largest ocean and is only a little smaller than the Atlantic. Because most of the water area of the Indian Ocean lies right on the equator, it is the warmest of the oceans overall and a major source of moisture for the South Asian summer monsoons.[13]

Thailand tsunami detection buoy floats in the Andaman sea, east of the Indian ocean for detection of tidal differentials that happen after underwater earthquakes.

© BNK Maritime Photographer/Shutterstock.com

The Arctic Ocean[14]

The Arctic Ocean, which covers the North Pole, is the smallest and shallowest of the world's oceans. It has been covered with a layer of ice about 30 feet thick through most of the year, though the extent of summer melting has been increasing since the early 2000s. The melting of the ice has been accompanied by an increase in shipping and cruising ships around the fringes of the Arctic Ocean. The countries bounding the Arctic Ocean have become more assertive in claiming territorial rights to potential ocean floor mineral resources.[15]

Arctic Icebergs in Arctic Ocean near Greenland.
© MrPhotoMania/Shutterstock.com

The Southern Ocean

The Southern Ocean is the newest ocean in terms of recognition, being designated by the International Hydrographic Organization in 2000. Although it appears to be the southern portions of the Atlantic, Indian and Pacific Oceans, it is functionally distinct from its adjacent oceans to the north. It includes all of the ocean waters south of 60° S latitude. Its dominant feature is the Antarctic Circumpolar Current, a continuous current of cold water and upper latitude cold fronts that encircle the continent of Antarctica. The storms in the air above it have the strongest average winds in the world, making travel to Antarctica a challenge. A large portion of the Southern Ocean freezes in the Southern Hemisphere's winter months, when most of the ocean is without sunlight.[16]

Ocean Threats

Global warming, litter pollution, and overfishing are among the major threats to the oceans today. As the planet has increased in temperature since the 1960s, the oceans have also been getting warmer, causing massive ice melting in the polar regions and the death of vast areas of **coral** (a living animal) in many coastal areas. Ocean water levels, which vary around the world due to differences in the shape of the earth's crust, are also gradually increasing

Coral bleaching: dead reef from climate change, global warming, pollution and overfishing

© Rich Carey/Shutterstock.com

and causing more frequent flooding of coastal lands and settlements. These disasters could affect up to one billion people in the coming century.[17]

Climate Change and the Oceans

Ocean temperatures have a huge, and poorly-understood impact on climate and weather patterns. As large bodies of water, the oceans are slow to gain or lose heat (as opposed to continents, which gain and lose heat from the sun rapidly). Even if the earth were to stop warming now, it would take several decades for the oceans to cool again to the temperatures of past decades. In addition, ocean currents circulate warm and cold water across the surface of the planet, stabilizing the more dramatic temperature changes that occur on the earth's continents.[18]

Ocean Garbage Patches

Few unsightlier natural scenes exist than a beach, cluttered with litter and debris. Unfortunately, much debris is not from local sources but possibly from hundreds or thousands of miles away. Humans have long assumed that the ocean's vast size renders disposal of liquid and solid waste into them to be an act without consequence. Small fishing vessels to large cargo and cruise ships have historically spewed litter, oil, and sewage directly into the oceans, and many continue to do so today.[19]

Plastics and other refuse has washed ashore a remote island in the tropical western Pacific region. Plastics, in particular, are a serious threat to the marine ecosystem.

© Ethan Daniels/Shutterstock.com

Plastic bottle are all to common in the ocean sea water.

© Mr.anaked/Shutterstock.com

Urban settlements and coastal industrial activities have similarly used the oceans as open sewage pits. Plastics, in particular, can be fatal to marine life and require many decades to decay. Areas with the worst concentrations of plastics tend to be major coastal tourist destinations, like Europe, the U.S. the Caribbean and Indonesia. In addition, remote areas of the[20] Pacific,[21] Atlantic,[22] and Indian Oceans have developed massive[23]

ocean gyres, (or garbage patches), where small and large fragments of plastics accumulate and circulate thousands of miles from the nearest coastline,[24] due to a phenomenon called the Coriolis effect.

Overfishing

It is estimated that, in 1900, the oceans had six times as many fish than there are today. The greatest loss of fish has been of the larger, predatory species like tuna and cod. One of the reasons for this is that no one owns the open seas, which allows anyone with a large enough net to catch an unlimited number of fish. Overfishing in waters close to coastlines can be managed to some degree, though this depends on effective government actions.[25]

Fishing is an economic mainstay, but is often not regulated.

© KlavdiyaV/Shutterstock.com

The biggest threat to fishing comes from bottom trawling (bethnic trawling), in which massive nets are dragged along the bottom of the oceans, capturing or killing everything in the way. It is estimated that the amount of sea floor that is scraped by bottom trawling is 150 times the amount of forests that are clear-cut worldwide each year.

Industrial scale fishing of this kind is a major focus of government regulation and environmental groups. However, about 90% of the world's fishing is undertaken by small scale operators who depend on fish resources for the family's livelihood. Consumers awareness and better ocean and coastal management are essential for addressing the loss of our underwater marine populations and ecosystems.[26]

Ghost net (abandoned fishing net) pollution in the ocean environment.

© Rich Carey/Shutterstock.com

Review Terms

Antarctic Circle	Atlantic Ocean	ocean gyres
Antarctic Convergence	Challenger Deep	Pacific Ocean
Antarctic Treaty	coral	South Pole
Arctic Circle	Indian Ocean	Southern Ocean
Arctic Ocean	North Pole	

Research Topics

Drake Passage
glacier
ice cap
North Magnetic Pole
northeast passage
northwest passage
oceanography
ozone
polar easterlies
South Magnetic Pole
white-out

Credits

1. **Source:** From Alan A. Lew, C. Michael Hall, and Dallen J. Timothy, *World Regional Geography: Human Mobilities, Tourism, Destinations, Sustainable Environments*, 2nd ed., Copyright © 2015 by Kendall Hunt Publishing Company. Reprinted by permission.
2. **Source:** From Alan A. Lew, C. Michael Hall, and Dallen J. Timothy, *World Regional Geography: Human Mobilities, Tourism, Destinations, Sustainable Environments*, 2nd ed., Copyright © 2015 by Kendall Hunt Publishing Company. Reprinted by permission.
3. **Source:** From Alan A. Lew, C. Michael Hall, and Dallen J. Timothy, *World Regional Geography: Human Mobilities, Tourism, Destinations, Sustainable Environments*, 2nd ed., Copyright © 2015 by Kendall Hunt Publishing Company. Reprinted by permission.
4. **Source:** From Alan A. Lew, C. Michael Hall, and Dallen J. Timothy, *World Regional Geography: Human Mobilities, Tourism, Destinations, Sustainable Environments*, 2nd ed., Copyright © 2015 by Kendall Hunt Publishing Company. Reprinted by permission.
5. **Source:** From Alan A. Lew, C. Michael Hall, and Dallen J. Timothy, *World Regional Geography: Human Mobilities, Tourism, Destinations, Sustainable Environments*, 2nd ed., Copyright © 2015 by Kendall Hunt Publishing Company. Reprinted by permission.
6. **Source:** From Alan A. Lew, C. Michael Hall, and Dallen J. Timothy, *World Regional Geography: Human Mobilities, Tourism, Destinations, Sustainable Environments*, 2nd ed., Copyright © 2015 by Kendall Hunt Publishing Company. Reprinted by permission.
7. **Source:** From Alan A. Lew, C. Michael Hall, and Dallen J. Timothy, *World Regional Geography: Human Mobilities, Tourism, Destinations, Sustainable Environments*, 2nd ed., Copyright © 2015 by Kendall Hunt Publishing Company. Reprinted by permission.
8. **Source:** From Alan A. Lew, C. Michael Hall, and Dallen J. Timothy, *World Regional Geography: Human Mobilities, Tourism, Destinations, Sustainable Environments*, 2nd ed., Copyright © 2015 by Kendall Hunt Publishing Company. Reprinted by permission.
9. **Source:** From Alan A. Lew, C. Michael Hall, and Dallen J. Timothy, *World Regional Geography: Human Mobilities, Tourism, Destinations, Sustainable Environments*, 2nd ed., Copyright © 2015 by Kendall Hunt Publishing Company. Reprinted by permission.
10. **Source:** From Alan A. Lew, C. Michael Hall, and Dallen J. Timothy, *World Regional Geography: Human Mobilities, Tourism, Destinations, Sustainable Environments*, 2nd ed., Copyright © 2015 by Kendall Hunt Publishing Company. Reprinted by permission.
11. **Source:** From Alan A. Lew, C. Michael Hall, and Dallen J. Timothy, *World Regional Geography: Human Mobilities, Tourism, Destinations, Sustainable Environments*, 2nd ed., Copyright © 2015 by Kendall Hunt Publishing Company. Reprinted by permission.
12. **Source:** From Alan A. Lew, C. Michael Hall, and Dallen J. Timothy, *World Regional Geography: Human Mobilities, Tourism, Destinations, Sustainable Environments*, 2nd ed., Copyright © 2015 by Kendall Hunt Publishing Company. Reprinted by permission.

13. **Source:** From Alan A. Lew, C. Michael Hall, and Dallen J. Timothy, *World Regional Geography: Human Mobilities, Tourism, Destinations, Sustainable Environments*, 2nd ed., Copyright © 2015 by Kendall Hunt Publishing Company. Reprinted by permission.

14. **Source:** From Alan A. Lew, C. Michael Hall, and Dallen J. Timothy, *World Regional Geography: Human Mobilities, Tourism, Destinations, Sustainable Environments*, 2nd ed., Copyright © 2015 by Kendall Hunt Publishing Company. Reprinted by permission.

15. **Source:** From Alan A. Lew, C. Michael Hall, and Dallen J. Timothy, *World Regional Geography: Human Mobilities, Tourism, Destinations, Sustainable Environments*, 2nd ed., Copyright © 2015 by Kendall Hunt Publishing Company. Reprinted by permission.

16. **Source:** From Alan A. Lew, C. Michael Hall, and Dallen J. Timothy, *World Regional Geography: Human Mobilities, Tourism, Destinations, Sustainable Environments*, 2nd ed., Copyright © 2015 by Kendall Hunt Publishing Company. Reprinted by permission.

17. **Source:** From Alan A. Lew, C. Michael Hall, and Dallen J. Timothy, *World Regional Geography: Human Mobilities, Tourism, Destinations, Sustainable Environments*, 2nd ed., Copyright © 2015 by Kendall Hunt Publishing Company. Reprinted by permission.

18. **Source:** From Alan A. Lew, C. Michael Hall, and Dallen J. Timothy, *World Regional Geography: Human Mobilities, Tourism, Destinations, Sustainable Environments*, 2nd ed., Copyright © 2015 by Kendall Hunt Publishing Company. Reprinted by permission.

19. **Source:** From Alan A. Lew, C. Michael Hall, and Dallen J. Timothy, *World Regional Geography: Human Mobilities, Tourism, Destinations, Sustainable Environments*, 2nd ed., Copyright © 2015 by Kendall Hunt Publishing Company. Reprinted by permission.

20. **Source:** From Alan A. Lew, C. Michael Hall, and Dallen J. Timothy, *World Regional Geography: Human Mobilities, Tourism, Destinations, Sustainable Environments*, 2nd ed., Copyright © 2015 by Kendall Hunt Publishing Company. Reprinted by permission.

21. **Source:** From Alan A. Lew, C. Michael Hall, and Dallen J. Timothy, *World Regional Geography: Human Mobilities, Tourism, Destinations, Sustainable Environments*, 2nd ed., Copyright © 2015 by Kendall Hunt Publishing Company. Reprinted by permission.

22. **Source:** From Alan A. Lew, C. Michael Hall, and Dallen J. Timothy, *World Regional Geography: Human Mobilities, Tourism, Destinations, Sustainable Environments*, 2nd ed., Copyright © 2015 by Kendall Hunt Publishing Company. Reprinted by permission.

23. **Source:** From Alan A. Lew, C. Michael Hall, and Dallen J. Timothy, *World Regional Geography: Human Mobilities, Tourism, Destinations, Sustainable Environments*, 2nd ed., Copyright © 2015 by Kendall Hunt Publishing Company. Reprinted by permission.

24. **Source:** From Alan A. Lew, C. Michael Hall, and Dallen J. Timothy, *World Regional Geography: Human Mobilities, Tourism, Destinations, Sustainable Environments*, 2nd ed., Copyright © 2015 by Kendall Hunt Publishing Company. Reprinted by permission.

25. **Source:** From Alan A. Lew, C. Michael Hall, and Dallen J. Timothy, *World Regional Geography: Human Mobilities, Tourism, Destinations, Sustainable Environments*, 2nd ed., Copyright © 2015 by Kendall Hunt Publishing Company. Reprinted by permission.

26. **Source:** From Alan A. Lew, C. Michael Hall, and Dallen J. Timothy, *World Regional Geography: Human Mobilities, Tourism, Destinations, Sustainable Environments*, 2nd ed., Copyright © 2015 by Kendall Hunt Publishing Company. Reprinted by permission.